Calf Care

by Coleen Jones and
Jud Heinrichs

About the authors

Coleen Jones grew up on a dairy farm in western Pennsylvania where she was actively involved in 4-H, FFA, and dairy promotion. She attended Virginia Tech and earned a bachelor's degree in Dairy Science with a minor in Agricultural and Applied Economics. An internship with Hoard's Dairyman helped Coleen to decide to pursue a career in communications. She completed a master's degree in Dairy Management and Nutrition at Virginia Tech, focusing on the care and management of newborn calves and feeding of colostrum. She has been employed by The Pennsylvania State University since 2002 and assists with research and extension activities related to calves, heifers, and forages. Her primary interests include the health and growth of young dairy cattle, nutritional requirements of calves, and information management to improve decisions on the farm. She is a member of the American Dairy Science Association. Coleen and her husband Brian own a small, diversified farm in Craigsville, Virginia.

Jud Heinrichs is a professor of Dairy Science at Penn State and has been a member of the faculty for 24 years. He has a research and extension appointment in the area of dairy nutrition and feeding management. His research programs focus on dairy calves and heifers from a standpoint of nutrition and management. He also does some research in dairy cow feeding management and was a co-developer of the Penn State Particle Separator, a device used around the world by dairy nutritionists to better define forage and total mixed ration particle size. His extension work closely follows his research program and has a focus on feeding management and dairy replacements. Jud grew up on a small dairy farm in New York.

Contents

CALVING

Successful delivery of a live calf and proper care in the first few hours after birth are the first steps that put calves on the path to good health and growth. The goal is for them to enter the milking string as profitable replacement animals.

MAINTAIN THE MATERNITY AREA

The newborn calf first meets the outside world in the maternity area. Make every effort to limit the calf's exposure to pathogens here, because the calf is born with no protection from disease or infection. Keep the calving area clean and dry. Use either well-bedded pens or grassy pastures, and limit the time cows spend in the pen to 8 hours or less. Maternity areas are for calving—not for housing close-up cows.

Locate the maternity pen where cows are easy to observe regularly, and provide plenty of light and protection from drafts. Provide 144 to 150 square feet [13 to 14 sq. meters] of space per cow. Individual pens measuring 12 feet by 12 feet or 10 feet by 15 feet [3.66 by 3.66 or 3 by 4.6 meters] are preferred over group pens. It also is helpful to provide a method of restraining cows in case assistance is required during calving. A head catch hung low to the ground allows the cow to lie down without choking. Use of vertical bars rather than V-slants also reduces the choking hazard. Another option is tying the cow with a rope halter; be sure to tie her head low to the ground. Squeeze chutes are not recommended because they restrict movement too much.

Disinfect the maternity pens after each calving. During calving, 4 to 5 gallons [15 to 19 liters] of amniotic and allantoic fluid are expelled with the calf. This fluid contains large amounts of protein, sugar, urea, and fat, making it an excellent medium for bacterial growth. Fluids from birth also mix with manure, which may contain pathogenic organisms. That's why it's so important to remove all contaminated bedding and manure, and to clean surfaces with disinfectant. Apply lime to the floor to improve footing before adding a thick layer of dry bedding. If calves are born in a group pen, add enough fresh bedding daily to keep the surface clean and dry. Group pens must be cleaned at least weekly, although daily cleaning is preferred. The decision to use group calving pens should be made with the understanding that the risk of

A grassy pasture or well-bedded pen are preferred locations for calving. Bedding in a maternity pen should be deep and dry.

Limit the calving cow's time in the pen to 8 hours or less: the pen should be for calving, not a place to house close-up cows.

calf illness and death is greater than when individual pens are provided.

Bedding should be 6 to 8 inches [15 to 20 cm] deep and dry enough that after kneeling for at least one minute, your knees are dry. Sawdust is not recommended for bedding maternity areas because it can harbor bacteria that can infect the udder, uterus or navel. Sawdust particles can also irritate the lungs of newborn calves and contribute to respiratory problems.

EVENTS OF A NORMAL CALVING

Understanding the normal progression of events during calving and knowing when and how to assist an abnormal birth are essential to minimize calf deaths and cow losses. Cows undergo a series of hormonally-controlled changes that indicate the start of calving. Several weeks before freshening the udder fills with colostrum, and as calving approaches, the vulva becomes swollen, and pelvic ligaments relax, causing a sunken appearance around the tailhead. Mucus discharged from the vagina becomes flowing and clear, similar to the mucus observed during estrus. The actual birth process progresses through three continuous stages: preparation, delivery of the calf and passage of the fetal membranes.

During Stage 1, the cervix relaxes and dilates. The cow may act restless and seek solitude. She also may look at her flanks, stamp her feet, raise her tail, arch her back, and urinate or defecate frequently. Weak straining of the abdominal muscles can be seen as well. Stage 1 ends when the fetal membranes become visible. In cows this process may take 3 to 6 hours. Heifers may need 4 to 10 hours to prepare for delivery. During this time, observe animals hourly from a distance to monitor their progress.

Stage 2 begins when the "water bag" breaks. This is the chorioallantois, the outer membrane that surrounds the calf in the uterus. Once this membrane breaks, the legs and head of the calf begin to push through the cervix and into the vagina. The cow usually acts restless and repeatedly switches from standing to lying down. When the calf's feet enter the vagina, the inner membrane, called the amnion, breaks, releasing a thick, lubricating fluid. The time between the breaking of the first and second membranes is often about 1 hour. If the cow did not

ABOVE: Stage 2 of calving begins when the "water bag" breaks, followed by the inner membrane, the amnion. If the cow did not begin labor in a maternity pen, wait and move her there once the calf's feet are visible.

AT RIGHT: FIGURE 1.1. Normal birth position of the calf. The calf lies on its stomach with its forelegs extended and its heading lying on them. In this way, the calf is presented at its smallest diameter.

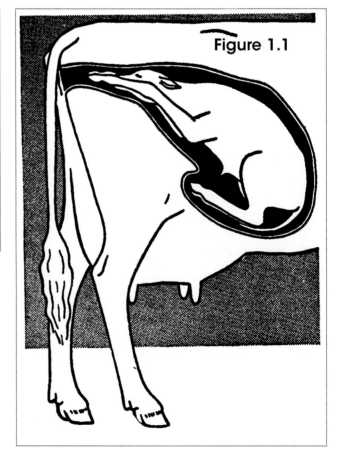

Figure 1.1

begin labor in a maternity pen, wait and move her there once the calf's feet are visible. Strong abdominal straining can be observed as uterine contractions become more frequent. Another delay occurs as the vulva is stretched by the head, which often slips in and out of sight. The cow continues to push until the head and shoulders are delivered, then typically rests for a few moments. Once straining resumes, the rest of the calf is usually delivered quickly. Most cows have their calves in 1 to 2 hours after the water breaks. Heifers may take 2 to 4 hours. During this stage, continue to observe the animal every 30 minutes.

The final stage, passage of the fetal membranes, is a continued series of uterine contractions and a rapid decrease in the size of the uterus, a process called involution. The attachment between the placenta and uterus relaxes, and the placenta separates from the uterus. Stage 3 ends with the passage of the fetal membranes, or

afterbirth. Normally, the placenta is passed within 1 to 8 hours after birth of the calf. A placenta that is not expelled within 12 hours is considered a retained placenta. Do not attempt to remove a retained placenta manually or insert anything into the uterus. Work with your veterinarian to develop a treatment plan for such cows.

DIFFICULT AND ABNORMAL BIRTHS

While the majority of cows and heifers calve normally with little assistance, roughly 6 percent of cows and 20 percent of heifers experience calving difficulty, or dystocia. In addition, 7 percent of calves are born dead or die within 48 hours of birth, and calving problems are a leading cause of death in cows. Stillborn births have actually increased somewhat in recent years, according to Iowa research. Dystocia is more common in heifers than cows because heifers are usually smaller and have not given birth before. When dystocia occurs in cows, the prob-

Work with your veterinarian to develop a treatment plan for cows with retained placentas.

lem is likely to be more serious, often due to a large or poorly positioned calf. Milk fever may pres-

FIGURE 1.2. Greater difficulty at calving increases the risk of calves dying during delivery or in the first 48 hours of life. This study analyzed single births only, twins were not included.

Adapted from Meyer et al, 2000. Journal of Dairy Science, 83:2657-2663.

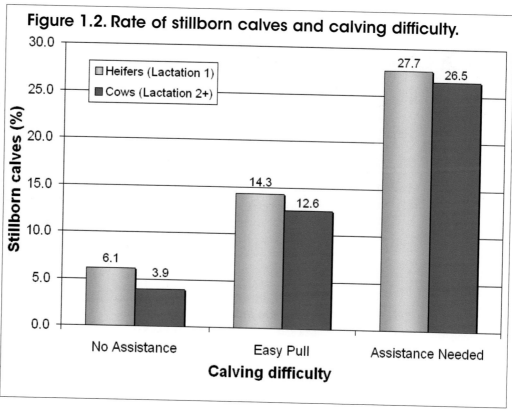

Figure 1.2. Rate of stillborn calves and calving difficulty.

Heifers (Lactation 1)
Cows (Lactation 2+)

Stillborn calves (%)

Calving difficulty	Heifers	Cows
No Assistance	6.1	3.9
Easy Pull	14.3	12.6
Assistance Needed	27.7	26.5

ent additional complications. Observation of calving and assisting when needed can reduce the number of stillborn calves and increase survival rates.

Calving difficulty scores (see sidebar) can be used to help track calving problems. As dystocia becomes more severe, calf deaths in the first 48 hours increase (Figure 1.2). Some causes of dystocia include age of the dam, large calves, small pelvic opening in the dam, weak contraction of the uterus (possibly linked to milk fever), abnormal position of the calf and twins. Pay attention to sire calving ease ratings, especially in small cows and first-calf heifers, and only use bulls with less than 10 percent calving difficulty on cows at high risk for dystocia. Besides heifers and small cows, those at high risk include cows with a history of reproductive problems (uterine torsion, prolapse or uterine tears) or metabolic disease (milk fever or ketosis). Fat animals also have increased dystocia risk, due to fatty deposits around the reproductive tract and pelvic area, and increased risk of metabolic disorders.

Examining the Cow

During Stage 1, examine animals if no progress has been made after 4 hours. If progress seems to stop after the water bag appears, animals should be examined to see if assistance is needed. Examine cows if they have made no progress an hour after the water bag first appears. For first-calf heifers, wait 2 hours after the water bag first appears before examining the animal.

Animals also should be examined if progress has stopped for more than 30 minutes after active straining. Rest periods typically last only 5 to 10 minutes and a lack of progress may indicate the calf is too large or the cow is weak. In most cases, there is no need to rush and immediately pull the calf; it can live for 8 to 10 hours after the first water bag breaks. The exception is a calf presented backward. In this case pressure on the umbilical cord can cut off the oxygen supply. Quickly assist all calves presented backward.

Before you start the exam, restrain the animal and tie her tail to her neck with a piece of twine to keep it out of the way. Thoroughly wash the anus, vulva, and pin bones with soap and water. Wash your arms and hands with disinfectant soap and apply generous amounts of lubricant to them. Avoid using soap as a lubricant because it removes the natural lubrication of the birth canal and can irritate and inflame vaginal membranes. Commercially available obstetrical lubricants containing methylcellulose are recommended. Mineral oil also may be used for lubrication. Form a cone with your fingers and thumb and gently push a hand into the vulva. Once in the vagina, the hand can be flattened with the palm facing down and pushed along the roof of the vagina.

The first step is to determine the extent of cervical dilation. The calf's body will stimulate dilation as it is delivered, but early in delivery the cervical opening must be wide enough to allow the nose and feet to pass easily. Next, determine what body parts of the calf are presented. Front legs can be distinguished from back legs by the direction the joint above the fetlock bends. If it bends in the same direction as the fetlock, it is the knee and a front leg. If it bends in the opposite direction, it is the hock and a back leg. The soles of the feet indicate the position of the calf; in a normal delivery soles on

Scoring Calving Difficulty

1 = No assistance

2 = Easy pull

3 = Hard pull

4 = Mechanical assistance (calf jack)

5 = Veterinary assistance or cesarean.

Dystocia = score of 3 or more

Figure 1.3. Determining the calf's position.

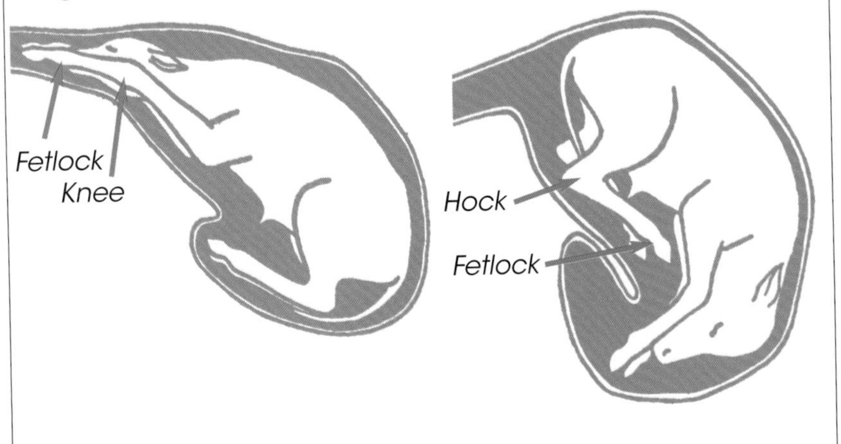

FIGURE 1.3. The direction the joints of the leg bend can be used to help figure out a calf's position. The fetlock joint bends in the same direction as the knee; this indicates you are feeling a front leg. The fetlock bends in the opposite direction of the hock; this indicates you have a back leg.

the front feet face down, soles on the back feet face up. Since twinning rates of up to 10 percent occur in some herds, be sure to find two legs and determine that they belong to one calf before pulling the calf. To find out if a pair of legs belongs to one calf, follow one leg to the brisket and then trace down the other leg. Also, determine the position of the head. In a normal forward delivery, the chin rests just above the knees (Figure 1.1, page 6). In uncomplicated backward delivery, the head will not be presented; the tail should be down and between the thighs.

Finally, consider the stress level of the calf. Determine if the calf is alive by pinching between the toes. Live calves will reflexively draw the foot back. Calves presented backward can be tested by inserting a finger into the rectum. Live calves will squeeze your finger. The only time to pull a calf presented in a normal position is when it is distressed. The color of the tongue is one indicator of stress. Normally, tongue color darkens during hard contractions and lightens between contractions. If the tongue stays dark through the rest period, the calf is in distress. If blood or pieces of the placenta appear, the calf likely is bleeding and should be pulled.

Once you have examined the animal and assessed the situation, determine whether you can assist with the delivery or extra help is needed. Three situations that call for help are: you cannot find the cause of the problem; you know the problem, but cannot solve it; you have been trying to correct the problem for 30 minutes and have made no progress. If any of these situations occur, find a more experienced person to help or call the veterinarian.

ABNORMAL BIRTH POSITIONS

If examination of the cow reveals an abnormal presentation, the situation must be corrected before delivery can occur. If the calf cannot be quickly manipulated into a normal position, obtain veterinary assistance. Do not attempt to pull a calf in an abnormal position; this may injure the cow, kill the calf or both.

Some abnormal positions are presented in Figure 1.4. Calves presented backward can be delivered, as long as the legs are stretched out behind the calf. However, a backward calf must be delivered quickly because the umbilical cord is pinched between the calf and the pelvis early in delivery. Pinching the cord slows blood circulation and may cause death or brain damage. To correct abnormal positions, it is often necessary to push the calf back into the uterus where the cow's pelvis

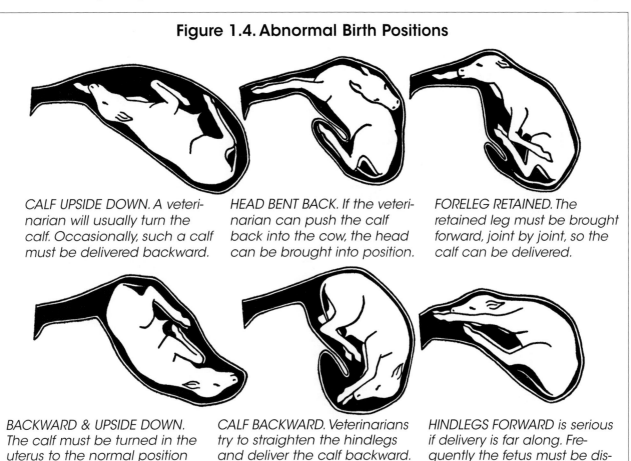

Figure 1.4. Abnormal Birth Positions

CALF UPSIDE DOWN. A veterinarian will usually turn the calf. Occasionally, such a calf must be delivered backward.

HEAD BENT BACK. If the veterinarian can push the calf back into the cow, the head can be brought into position.

FORELEG RETAINED. The retained leg must be brought forward, joint by joint, so the calf can be delivered.

BACKWARD & UPSIDE DOWN. The calf must be turned in the uterus to the normal position for delivery.

CALF BACKWARD. Veterinarians try to straighten the hindlegs and deliver the calf backward.

HINDLEGS FORWARD is serious if delivery is far along. Frequently the fetus must be dismembered.

will not interfere with manipulation. Before moving the calf, attach obstetric chains to one leg to enable retrieval. Between straining episodes, firmly push the calf back and manipulate it into the correct position. When moving a foot, place your hand over the hoof to prevent tearing the birth canal. It is essential to determine the exact position before attempting to correct it. Correcting anything more than a turned leg or head usually requires veterinary assistance.

ASSISTING DELIVERY

Most births do not require assistance. Rushing delivery can injure the cow and should be avoided. However, waiting too long after the water breaks to assist may deprive the calf of oxygen and cause death. When it is necessary to assist, use the following techniques to increase the number of live calves born and decrease injuries to cows.

First, remember to wash the external genitalia of the cow and wash and lubricate your hands and arms. Keep two buckets of warm water nearby, one to wash the cow and one to wash your hands and arms and store obstetrical chains and handles. The birth canal may be dilated manually to assist delivery and minimize tearing injuries. To do this, insert both arms into the vulva and vagina, clasp your hands and bend your elbows outward to stretch the birth canal.

Attach obstetrical chains to both legs, making two loops, one above and one below the fetlock joint as shown in Figure 1.5. Position chains to pull from the underside of legs. Pull one leg out until the pastern is about four inches [10 cm] outside the vulva. While holding the leg in this position, pull the other leg out to the same distance. Pulling both legs at once may cause the calf's shoulders (or hips in a backwards delivery) to lodge in the pelvic opening as illustrated in Figure 1.6. If the shoulders lock in the pelvis, place a rope or chain around the calf's poll and through the mouth as shown in Figure 1.7. Pulling on the calf's head in this manner reduces the size of the shoulders and chest and may loosen the calf.

Once the head and shoulders have been delivered, rotate the calf about half a turn. This allows the widest part of the calf's hips to pass through the widest part of the cow's pelvis as shown in Figure 1.6. Without rotation, the calf's hips pass through the narrowest part of the cow's pelvis, which may result in hiplock. If pressure continues after hiplock, the cow can suffer nerve damage or tearing of the reproductive tract. If the calf is coming backward, rotation must be accomplished as soon as the legs are available, because the hips will come through the pelvis next. To be effective, rotation must occur before the hips enter the pelvic opening. If hiplock occurs, push the calf back and rotate it before pulling again.

The direction and strength of extraction are also critical. Initially, pull straight back to move the calf into the pelvis. Once the head is delivered, pull downward in an arc toward the udder to slide the calf through the birth canal more easily. In a backward

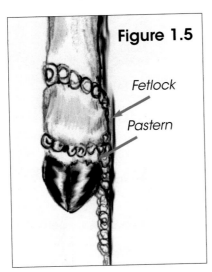

Figure 1.5

Fetlock

Pastern

FIGURE 1.5. Placement of leg chains for calving assistance.
Adapted from: Whittier and Thorne, 1995.

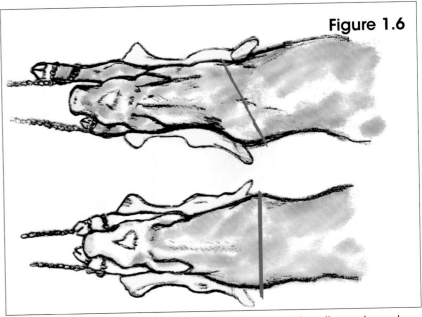

Figure 1.6

FIGURE 1.6. Correct technique for pulling a calf: pull one leg at a time (top) to avoid wedging shoulders in the pelvis (bottom).
Adapted from: Whittier and Thorne, 1995.

delivery, change the pulling direction once the base of the tail is delivered. Too much force can tear the birth canal or break the calf's legs or ribs; so no more than two people should pull on a calf. Extraction force should never exceed 400 pounds [180 kg]; a strong person can exert about 200 pounds [90 kg] of force. Calving gauges are available that measure the force exerted. To prevent injuries to the cow, pull on the calf only when the cow strains. Do not allow the calf to slip back into the cow in between straining, but do not exert force while the cow rests. Instead, use rest periods to reposition the calf if necessary.

Mechanical pullers or calf jacks are a last resort and should be used only by an experienced person. Applying excessive force is very easy when using a jack as many can exert 2,000 pounds [900 kg] or more. Pullers that work off of the cow, rather than a stationary object, are preferable. This allows movement with the cow and may change the pelvic angle and open the birth canal. Once the last rib is outside the vulva, stop pulling and allow the cow to finish the delivery.

TWINS NOT A BONUS

About five percent of calvings by dairy cows result in twins. Twinning is usually associated with greater dystocia, and the calves tend to be small and weak at birth. Twin calves have a greater risk of being stillborn and are more likely to die before weaning than calves born singly. Heifers born twin to a bull are sterile about 92 percent of the time. The reproductive tract of these heifers, called freemartins, is undeveloped as a result of exposure to male hormones during fetal growth. Bull calves may also be sub-fertile when born twin to a heifer. Having twins puts cows at a higher risk for many problems as well. These cows experience more abortions and greater problems at calving, and are more likely to have a retained placenta, metritis, displaced abomasum or ketosis. As a result, they are more difficult to breed back and more likely to be culled in the following lactation.

CARE OF THE NEWBORN CALF

Clearing the nasal passage, dipping the navel, and feeding colostrum are essential to raising healthy calves. Start calves off

right by taking a few minutes to do these things at birth. Once the calf is delivered, check to be sure it is breathing. If not, check for a heartbeat by placing a hand on the chest between the front legs; calves can be revived if the heart is still beating. Insert a clean piece of straw into the calf's nose to make it sneeze: this will clear mucus from its nose and stimulate breathing. Clear mucus from the calf's mouth, if needed, using clean fingers. If sticking a straw up the nose does not initiate breathing, throwing cold water over the calf's head may start respiration.

Sit the calf up on its knees to make it easier for the lungs to expand. Allow the cow to lick the calf dry or rub it down for several minutes using a towel or blanket. This stimulates the calf's circulation, removes moisture, and fluffs the hair, which reduces heat loss. Take the calf's temperature within 15 minutes of birth: if it is less than 101°F [38.3°C], the calf should be warmed under a blanket or heat lamp. Dip the calf's navel in 7 percent tincture of iodine to wash, disinfect, and begin drying it. Move the calf to a clean, well-bedded, draft-free pen or hutch. Even

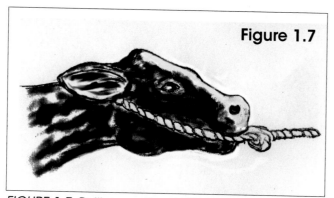

FIGURE 1.7. Pulling on the calf's head as shown reduces the size of the calf's shoulders and chest.
Adapted from: Practical Techniques for Dairy Farmers.

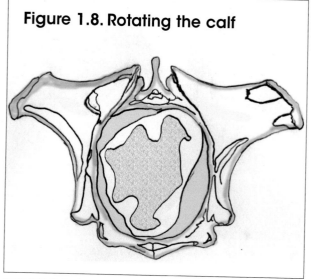

FIGURE 1.8. Align the widest part of the calf's hips with the widest part of the cow's pelvis.
Adapted from: Practical Techniques for Dairy Farmers.

during cold temperatures, dry, healthy calves can be moved directly to cold housing or hutches. Prolonging the move increases the risk of infection from dirty maternity areas or the dam, and allows the calf to adapt to the maternity area environment. Calves must then adapt to the new environment of their housing. Minimize stress on the calf by moving it to its preweaning home as soon as possible after birth.

Once you are sure the calf is alive and healthy, check the cow for a twin and make sure she is healthy. If she has not already stood up, get her to stand and offer her warm water to drink.

DIP THE NAVEL OF EVERY CALF

It is difficult to overstate the importance of dipping the calf's navel. The umbilical cord is a direct path to the calf's circulatory system. If bacteria infect the umbilical stump, they can travel throughout the body and the resulting infection is often lethal.

Calves are born into environments that contain bacteria; we cannot avoid this, but it is important to minimize the number of bacteria in calving areas and calf housing. Dipping the navel in 7 percent tincture of iodine washes off manure, urine, and dirt, kills bacteria, and, because the iodine is in an alcohol solution, dries out the umbilical cord.

Be sure to use tincture of iodine, not dilute iodine solutions. Weaker solutions do not kill bacteria as well and may not contain alcohol to dry out the cord. Dipping navels is recommended over spraying, as dipping assures complete coverage, while it's easy to miss an area with spraying. The navel can be dipped again 12 hours after birth to ensure complete drying. Continue to dip calves with no visible cord or thick cords for two to three days to fully dry the area around the umbilical stump.

Dipping navels is easy to do and costs very little, but the pay-back for dipping the navel of every calf is high, as calves are less likely to get sick. However, keep in mind that even repeated navel dipping cannot overcome infections picked up in a dirty calving pen, or a dip solution that is contaminated.

DON'T PUT OFF WEIGHING AND IDENTIFICATION

Weighing calves at birth allows accurate calculation of milk or milk replacer quantities to feed and medication doses. Establishing birth weights is the starting point for calculating daily weight gain. Birth weights also help evaluate dry cow and heifer nutrition programs and effectiveness of sire selection (using dystocia scores, for example). If a weight tape is used, use one specifically designed for calves, as the calibration is more accurate than tapes designed for cows.

Animal identification will soon be required as part of a national tracking system to ensure a safe

Dip the navel of every calf. Be careful not to roll the calf over and let bedding or dirt touch the navel area. If you use a Dixie cup as a disposable dipper, you'll keep your dip solution clean and uncontaminated.

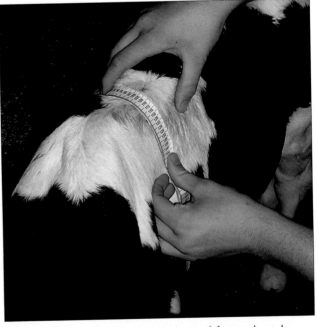

Use a tape specifically designed for calves to obtain the calf's birth weight. You then can calculate proper feeding or medication doses.

food supply. In addition, individual identification is essential for decision making, record keeping, and registration. Each calf should receive individual identification as soon after birth as possible, preferably before leaving the dam. Daily decisions, such as grouping, breeding and merchandising, as well as records of production, health and reproduction events, require accurate identification. Identification also is essential for developing accurate genetic evaluations of bulls and cows and to avoid inbreeding that reduces milk production, increases mortality and depresses fertility. Each calf needs immediate permanent and visible identification.

Permanent identification in the form of sketches, photos, tattoos and branding maintains animal identity, but more visible identification, such as ear tags, neck chains, or ankle bands, is more practical for everyday use. Choose visible identification that is easy to read without restraining the animal. The calf's permanent and visible identification should be recorded, along with identification of the sire and dam, date of birth, calving difficulty and birth weight.

GIVE VACCINATIONS AND CHECK CALF HEALTH

Soon after birth, calves may be given oral vaccines to prevent infections from *E. coli*, rota-, and coronavirus and intranasal vaccines against IBR and PI-3. In addition, vitamins A, D, and E and possibly selenium may be administered to prevent deficiencies. Consult your veterinarian for recommendations about these practices. Calf vaccination likely will

not be needed if cows are vaccinated before calving, the calving area is clean and calves receive adequate colostrum. Vitamins and selenium may not be necessary if the dam has adequate nutrition that maintains these nutrients at high levels in her blood.

When calves are born they often have bluish-gray tint to their gums and nose. By 30 minutes after birth, this should disappear and the gums and nose will change to a healthy pink color. Make note of anything unusual including: swelling of the head or tongue, dopey behavior, cloudy or bloody eyes, head held back, arched back, puffy abdomen, bleeding from any opening, labored breathing or broken ribs. Mark these calves and watch them closely as they may be more prone to develop health problems.

At birth body temperature is 103 to 104°F [39.4 to 40°C]. It drops within a half hour, and should stabilize near 101.5°F [38.6°C] by one hour. At this point most calves also are able to stand. It is impor-

---

Colostrum Q-Q-T Rule
(Quality-Quantity-Timing)

Quality

IgG – 50 mg/ml
Bacteria – < 100,000 cfu/ml
Fecal coliforms –
< 10,000 cfu/ml

Quantity

Large breeds: 2 feedings of
3 qts (3 l.) each
Small breeds: 2 feedings of
2 qts. (2 l.) each

Timing

First feeding within
1 hour of birth;
Second feeding
8 hours later.

---

tant that the calf is placed in its permanent calf housing by this time to allow it to adjust in that environment. If the calf's temperature is less than 100°F [36.3°C], put it under a heat lamp, blanket or calf jacket to be warmed.

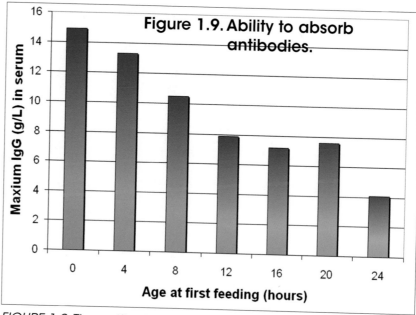

FIGURE 1.9. The calf's ability to absorb antibodies declines rapidly over the first 24 hours. As shown, calves fed two quarts of colostrum absorbed almost twice as many antibodies when fed at birth compared to those fed 12 hours after birth; and four times as many compared to calves first fed at 24 hours.
Adapted from Stott et al, 1979, Journal of Dairy Science, 62:1766-1773.

COLOSTRUM – THE ESSENTIAL FIRST MEAL

Colostrum is the first milk produced after a normal dry period, or the first milk secreted by a heifer. Unlike human babies, calves acquire no immunity during gestation. Colostrum is the source of passive immune protection that is essential for keeping the calf healthy. Colostrum is vital to a newborn calf's survival and should be fed as soon as possible after birth.

As the newborn's first food source, colostrum also provides nutrients to increase metabolism and stimulate digestive activity. Colostrum contains twice as much dry matter; three times as many minerals; and five times as much protein as whole milk. It is also much higher in energy and vitamins, in low reserve and needed by the newborn calf.

The importance of colostrum's immunoglobulins (antibodies) to the newborn calf cannot be overstated. Antibodies cannot cross the placental wall and pass directly from the cow to the fetus. Instead, the calf receives immunity to infectious diseases by consuming colostrum within the first few hours after birth. During the first 24 hours after birth, the calf can absorb antibodies intact; they escape digestion and pass directly into the bloodstream. This protection transferred from the dam to the calf via colostrum is called passive immunity, and it protects the calf until her own immune system becomes fully functional.

The amount of antibodies needed to effectively protect the calf will vary depending on the pathogen load in the environment and in colostrum, stress, housing and feeding practices. Other factors include the calf's size and the efficiency of IgG absorption. It is important to remember that feeding a large volume of colostrum cannot overcome low antibody concentration or high bacterial contamination. Volume is not the only factor determining the successful transfer of immunity from cow to calf.

RACING THE CLOCK

Feed large breed calves three quarts [3 liters] of undiluted colostrum within one hour of birth, and another three quarts eight hours later. Feed small breed calves two quarts [2 liters] of undiluted colostrum as soon as possible after birth, and another two quarts eight hours later. An alternative to this feeding schedule can be used when a second feeding of colostrum is not possible. In this case, feed four quarts [4 liters] of colostrum in a single feeding. Since many calves will not or cannot drink this large amount at one time, an esophageal feeder may be used to feed all or part of the colostrum. However, this method may increase the risk of calf death due to improper placement of the esophageal feeder, damage to the esophagus, and decreased efficiency of antibody absorption. Because it increases the stress

---

Factors affecting colostrum IgG levels

• First milking volume—cows that produce a large quantity of colostrum (greater than 18 pounds, or about 2 gallons; 8 liters) often produce lower concentrations of antibodies, likely due to dilution.

• Immune status of the dam—as it relates to her disease exposure and vaccination history.

• Length of the dry period—a 3 to 4 week dry period is needed to allow antibodies from the blood to be concentrated in colostrum.

• Age of the cow, especially as it relates to increased exposure to pathogens—most 2-year-old cows have antibodies to only a small number of pathogens.

• Dry cow nutrition—cows fed too little protein or energy tend to produce lower quality colostrum than cows fed adequately.

• Leaking milk prepartum or milking before calving—both reduce antibody levels; by colostrum removal or by dilution.

• Time between calving and first milking—IgG levels in colostrum decline rapidly after calving. Milk cows as soon as possible after calving.

• Breed—Jerseys tend to have the highest levels of antibodies, Holsteins the lowest, and other breeds fall in the middle.

• Season of the year—may be related to added stress and forage quality. Temperature extremes are problematic. In the north, late winter is often associated with poor quality. In the south, summer's heat and hot temperatures have been associated with lower quality colostrum.

placed on calves, this method is recommended only as a last resort.

Allowing the calf to nurse the cow is an unreliable feeding method. When calves are allowed to nurse on their own, 40 percent do not drink enough colostrum and only 25 percent consume adequate colostrum within an hour of birth.

Timing of colostrum feeding is critically important for two reasons: the calf's temporary ability to absorb large molecules and the potential for pathogenic bacteria to invade the intestine. By about 24 hours of age, the cells lining the intestine can no longer absorb large molecules intact. In addition, digestive enzyme secretion, which remains low for a limited time after birth, increases by about 12 hours and begins to break down antibodies in the gut. The longer we wait to feed first colostrum, the greater the chance calves will not receive enough immune protection (Figure 1.9). At best, only 25 to 30 percent of the antibodies a calf consumes ever reach the bloodstream—even when colostrum is fed immediately. If we wait six hours to feed, the average ability of the gut walls to absorb immunoglobulins decreases by one third. By 24 hours, the cells absorb less than 10 percent of what could originally be absorbed. Stressed calves typically have even less time to absorb antibodies than normal calves.

However, even if they cannot be absorbed into the blood, antibodies in colostrum may help fight infectious organisms in the calf's gut beyond 24 hours. The unabsorbed antibodies line the calf's intestinal tract, providing a protective coating that prevents bacteria from attaching to the gut

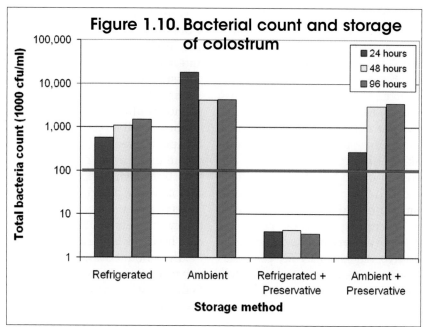

FIGURE 1.10. Bacteria can multiply rapidly in colostrum. Colostrum contained about 97,00 cfu/ml before storage by one of four methods. As shown above, refrigeration alone could not keep bacteria levels below 100,000 cfu/ml. Refrigeration plus added potassium sorbate preservative allowed storage up to 4 days.
Adapted from: Stewart et al, 2005. Journal of Dairy Science, 88:2571-2578.

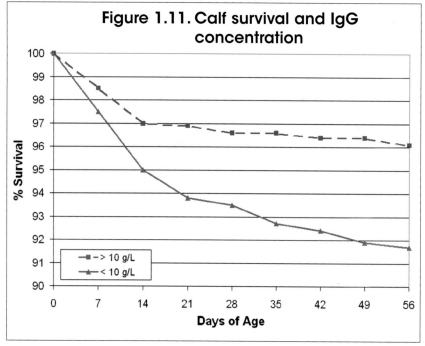

FIGURE 1.11. Calf survival to 2 months of age by serum IgG concentration: Calves with adequate passive transfer (IgG > 10 g/L) are more than twice as likely to survive to weaning compared to calves with failure of passive transfer (IgG < 10 g/L).
Source: USDA: NAHMS, 1993. National Dairy Heifer Evaluation Project.

wall. Unfortunately, this defense mechanism is of little value if bacteria enter the digestive tract first. Bacteria such as *E. coli* can attach to the gut walls and limit the attachment and absorption of antibodies. Early bacterial invasion of the gut creates another problem: immature intestinal cells can absorb infectious organisms as well as antibodies. If bacteria enter the bloodstream before antibodies, the calf has an extremely high risk of becoming sick or possibly dying. Therefore, colostrum, calves and the calving environment must be kept as clean as possible.

ANTIBODY CONCENTRATION IS IMPORTANT

Two factors dictate colostrum quality: antibody concentration (primarily immunoglobulin G, or IgG) and the presence or absence of bacteria. In terms of IgG, high quality colostrum contains at least 50 milligrams of IgG per milliliter (mg/ml). Note that IgG concentration also may be reported in grams per liter (g/L), which is equivalent to mg/ml. Management practices have limited control over IgG concentration, but it can be measured easily and feeding practices can be adjusted around it. On the other hand, proper management can ensure low bacterial loads and high quality, clean colostrum.

IgG concentration in colostrum varies tremendously due to a variety of factors; see the sidebar on page 14 for some examples. Colostrum IgG can easily range from 20 to 100 mg/ml, which can mean the difference between adequate immunity and failure of passive transfer (inadequate immunity).

Cows tend to produce antibodies in response to pathogens to which they have been exposed. Cows exposed to more pathogens produce colostrum with more antibodies than cows exposed to fewer diseases. For this reason, older cows often produce colostrum with a greater number and variety of antibodies than younger cows. However, if older cows are not exposed to many pathogens, their colostrum may not have high levels of antibodies. Heifers raised on other farms, where they are not exposed to the same pathogens as lactating cows, also produce inferior colostrum. An older cow on your farm produces the best quality colostrum for your calves, and a first-calf heifer raised at another location and moved to the farm a few days before freshening produces the poorest.

A good dry cow and heifer vaccination program can improve colostrum quality because vaccines stimulate maternal antibody production. These antibodies are then transferred to colostrum and provide calves with additional passive immunity. In contrast, vaccinating young calves produces a weak immune response because the immune system is not yet fully developed and cannot produce antibodies until 3 to 4 weeks of age. Even after the system is able to respond, the initial reaction to any vaccination is slow compared to response to a booster. Therefore, dry cow vaccination can be the most effective way to protect calves from infections common in the first 2 to 3 weeks of life, such as *E. coli*, rotavirus, coronavirus, and clostridial diseases.

The timing of dry cow vaccinations directly affects the success of increasing antibodies in colostrum. Antibodies from the cow's blood are actively secreted into colostrum in the last 1 to 2 weeks before calving. **So vaccination must occur at least 3 weeks before calving** to provide the cow time to respond to the vaccine and then transfer antibodies from her blood to her colostrum. Vaccination of first-calf heifers requires an initial

> ## Pathogens that spread through colostrum or milk from cow to calf
> - *Mycobacterium paratuberculosis (Johnes)*
> - *BVD virus*
> - *Bovine leukosis virus*
> - *E. coli*
> - *Salmonella species*
> - *Mycoplasma species*
> - *Pasteurella species*
> - *Staph. aureus*
>
> *Fecal contamination of milk increases risk of transfer and may add other environmental pathogens.*

vaccination at 6 or 7 weeks before calving and a booster 3 to 4 weeks before calving.

At least two other situations can result in a similar problem. If a cow calves well before her expected due date, she may not have enough time to respond to vaccinations, or may miss them entirely. Likewise, new animals that are transferred to the home farm just before calving may not have adequate time to be exposed to the herd's unique pathogens and mount an immune response to them before colostrum is formed. Allow at least 6 to 8 weeks of exposure to the herd before calving. In both cases, consider using stored colostrum for the first feeding.

CLEANLINESS IS A VIRTUE

Although colostrum quality is typically expressed in terms of IgG, contaminants also influence quality. Obviously, fewer contaminants mean higher quality. Some potential contaminants include blood, bacteria and remnants of mastitis infections (white blood cells, infectious organisms and antibiotic residues). Mastitic or excessively bloody colostrum must be discarded to avoid transferring pathogens to calves. Some diseases also can be transferred from cow to calf through colostrum (see the sidebar for examples). For this reason, do not feed colostrum from cows with known infections.

The potential for bacterial contamination of colostrum is not limited to bacteria in the cow's udder. Good, clean colostrum can be ruined if a cow's udder and teats are not well cleaned, sanitized and dried before the initial milking or nursing. Cracked or dirty teat-cup liners, hoses and gaskets can harbor bacteria too. Clean and maintain milking equipment regularly, especially bucket milk cans and their lids. Although this equipment is often ignored as it does not affect the quality of milk shipped, it should be cleaned and sanitized following the same procedures as other milking equipment to minimize bacterial contamination of colostrum.

Another key to keeping bacteria levels in check is feeding or cooling colostrum as soon as possible (within 30 minutes of milking). The warm, nutrient-rich liquid is an excellent environment for bacteria to grow. Bacteria counts of less than 100,000 colony-forming units per milliliter (cfu/ml) are considered acceptable, but research has shown that 36 to 82 percent of colostrum samples tested exceeded this level of bacterial contamination. In a Minnesota study, 53 percent of colostrum samples had more than one million bacteria per milliliter. In warm colostrum, bacteria can double in just 20 minutes. Even cooler temperatures can allow continued bacterial growth if cooling is slow. The same problem with bacterial growth can occur after frozen colostrum is thawed. Calves fed colostrum with high levels of bacteria have reduced passive transfer and greater incidence of disease in the first two weeks of life.

Try to cool colostrum to 40°F [4.5°C] or less as soon as possible; two simple physics concepts can help. First maximize the surface area exposed to cooler temperatures by putting colostrum into smaller containers. It's difficult to quickly cool colostrum that's in five gallon buckets, even those partially full. Second, maximize the temperature difference between your colostrum and the cooling source. Consider dropping clean jugs of ice into a large bucket of colostrum, or putting colostrum in bottles, then putting the bottles in a vat of ice water. Remember, any equipment that comes in contact with colostrum must be cleaned and sanitized regularly. In addition, be sure refrigerator function can be regularly monitored by equipping the unit with an easy-to-read thermometer.

MEASURE COLOSTRUM QUALITY

Large variation in colostrum quality can make feeding and managing this critical feed challenging. Although high-quality colostrum is typically very thick and creamy, appearance alone does not reliably predict quality. You can evaluate the effectiveness of your colostrum feeding and handling practices by monitoring colostrum IgG and bacteria levels and by measuring passive transfer of immunity. Lab tests can accurately measure the amount of IgG in colostrum, but these tests are expensive and time-consuming. Fortunately, there are ways to quickly estimate colostrum IgG content. One method relies on an instrument called a colostrometer that measures the specific gravity of colostrum and relates it to antibody concentration. Another method of testing colostrum is a cow-side kit that provides results in 20 minutes and classifies colostrum IgG concentrations as adequate (greater than 50 mg/ml)

or inadequate (less than 50 mg/ml).

The colostrometer is a hydrometer with a scale calibrated in milligrams per milliliter (mg/ml) of immunoglobulins. The colostrometer is placed in a cylinder containing colostrum and allowed to float freely. Colostrum quality is read from a color-coded scale and categorized as superior, acceptable, or unacceptable for feeding newborn calves. Superior readings (green) range from 50 to 140 mg/ml or more, acceptable readings (yellow) range from 20 to 50

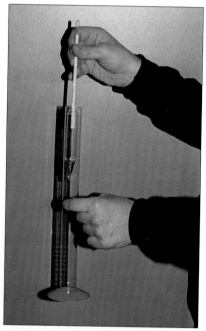

Similar to a hydrometer used to test auto batteries, the colostrometer is a practical way to measure colostrum quality. The one pictured is calibrated with a green, yellow and red scale. The level at which the colostrometer floats indicates the amount of immune-producing substances in the colostrum milk. Green is superior, yellow is moderate and red is inferior.
Photo courtesy of NASCO.

mg/ml, and unacceptable values (red) fall below 20 mg/ml of immunoglobulins. Colostrum testing "green" can be fed to newborn calves or stored for future use. Avoid feeding any other colostrum during the first or second feeding; fair or poor colostrum can be mixed with transition milk and fed to calves that are at least two days of age.

For greatest accuracy, measure colostrum IgG concentration using colostrum cooled to room temperature (72°F; 22°C). At lower temperatures, the colostrometer overestimates the IgG concentration; at temperatures above 72°F immunoglobulin concentrations will be underestimated. See Appendix 1 for a method of correcting colostrometer readings based on colostrum temperature. It is important to remember that colostrum is a wonderful medium for bacterial growth. If an entire milking of colostrum is left to cool for two hours before measuring the IgG level, bacteria have had ample opportunity to multiply. Avoid rapid bacterial growth by pouring a sample of the colostrum into the measuring cylinder and chilling the remaining colostrum immediately.

When troubleshooting calf health problems, it may be helpful to collect samples of colostrum at various stages of the handling, feeding, and storage process and determine bacteria counts. Ask your veterinarian to run a standard plate count and fecal coliform count on the samples. This will enable you to locate potential problems in udder preparation; colostrum collection, feeding, or storage containers; or thawing procedures that lead to increased bacterial growth. Remember to test samples at several points, including colostrum fed to calves.

STORE EXCESS COLOSTRUM

Storing excess high-quality colostrum allows you to collect surplus colostrum that can be used when good quality, fresh colostrum is not available for a newborn calf. Refrigeration (at 33 to 35°F [0.6 to 1.7°C]) can preserve colostrum quality for no more than 24 hours before bacterial growth reaches unacceptable levels (Figure 1.10). Potassium sorbate can be added to refrigerated colostrum to preserve it for up to four days. For long-term colostrum storage, freezing is the best alternative. Colostrum may be frozen (at -5°F [-21°C]) for up to a year without significant loss of antibodies. Frost-free freezers are not recommended for long-term colostrum storage, as they go through repeated freeze-thaw cycles that can markedly reduce IgG viability and shorten colostrum storage life.

One-gallon plastic bags with zipper-closure or two-quart bottles are excellent storage containers for freezing colostrum. Lay bags flat to increase their surface area, this maximizes storage space and minimizes freezing and thawing times. When needed, frozen colostrum can be placed in warm water (less than 120°F [49°C]) and allowed to thaw. Alternately, it can be thawed in a microwave oven with little damage to the antibodies. It is important to microwave colostrum for short periods on low power and pour off liquid periodically to minimize heating. It is also important to avoid "hot spots" inside frozen colostrum. Use of a turntable can help to minimize antibody damage. To provide a back-up plan when the dam's colostrum is of questionable quality or must be discarded, keep enough frozen colostrum on hand to feed several calves

Research shows that calves fed frozen colostrum have IgG levels similar to those fed fresh colostrum. However, fresh colostrum does have more leukocytes,

Allowing the calf to nurse is not reliable. Feed colostrum within one hour of birth and again eight hours later.

or white blood cells, which can help the newborn calf fight pathogens. While the higher white blood cell counts are an added benefit of feeding fresh colostrum, the amount of IgG in the colostrum, whether fresh or frozen, is the most important factor affecting calf immunity.

COLOSTRUM SUPPLEMENTS

Colostrum supplements can be used to increase the amount of IgG fed to calves when no source of quality colostrum is available. However, supplements cannot replace high quality colostrum. They do not contain sufficient quantities of antibodies to raise the blood IgG level in calves beyond what average quality colostrum will do. Follow the manufacturer's feeding instructions; some of these products are mixed with water and fed in an extra feeding, others are added to colostrum.

When comparing products, consider both the amount of IgG provided and the efficiency of IgG absorption. Supplement products based on bovine serum contain high levels of IgG and have absorption efficiencies similar to colostrum (25 to 35 percent). Products based on colostrum or whey have variable IgG contents and absorption efficiencies ranging from 5 to 30 percent. Egg-based supplements to date are not well-absorbed, but can provide local protection in the intestine.

COLOSTRUM REPLACERS

Products designed to replace colostrum are now available. These serum-based products contain at least 100 grams of IgG per liter plus fat, protein, vitamins, and minerals needed by the newborn calf. Colostrum replacer has more immunoglobulin than supplement products and provides more antibodies than poor or moderate quality colostrum. In research trials, calves fed colostrum replacer have performed as well as calves fed maternal colostrum with no differences in IgG levels, efficiency of IgG absorption, incidence of scours or growth rates. High quality maternal colostrum is still the "gold standard" for feeding newborn calves. However, colostrum replacer can be fed to reduce the spread of disease. For examples of pathogens transferred by milk, see the sidebar on page 16. When colostrum supplies are limited, colostrum replacer provides an effective, convenient method of providing passive immunity to calves.

PASTEURIZATION OF COLOSTRUM

Pasteurizing colostrum before feeding is possible but it can be difficult. Colostrum is a thick liquid that may not heat uniformly, allowing more organisms to survive. At the same time, pasteurization destroys immunoglobulins: IgG levels in colostrum are reduced by about 25 percent after pasteurization, according to research. Colostrum with high concentrations of IgG suffers greater IgG losses than lower quality colostrum, but retains a higher concentration in the final

One-gallon plastic bags are a convenient way to freeze and store colostrum. Thawing can be accomplished in warm water or on low power in a microwave.

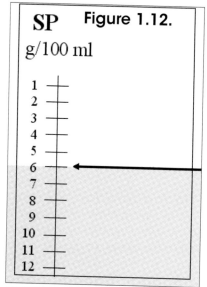

FIGURE 1.12. Sample of the scale inside a refractometer. Look for the scale designed for protein (measured in grams per deciliter or 100 milliliters). Read the scale at the interface between the light and dark areas; in this case 6 g/dl (or 100 ml).

feed. Pasteurization may affect IgG losses more if heating time is extended due to large batches or recycling of colostrum that failed to reach the correct temperature.

Commercially available batch and continuous-flow pasteurization methods can effectively kill most infectious organisms (including *Mycobacterium paratuberculosis*) in colostrum. However, the success of on-farm pasteurization is strongly related to management of the system. Key items to remember are:

1) start with high quality colostrum (60 mg/ml of IgG);

2) maintain strict sanitation of colostrum and pasteurization equipment;

3) chill colostrum pre- and post-pasteurization if it is not used immediately;

4) monitor the time and temperature of pasteurization and cleaning processes, and

5) test bacteria levels (before and after pasteurization) periodically.

Colostrum may present problems for cleaning pasteurization equipment and in some cases may clog the pasteurizer. When carefully managed, colostrum can be successfully pasteurized; however, due to the potential inactivation of immunoglobulins, pasteurization is considered a last resort to be tried when frozen colostrum or colostrum replacer are not feasible alternatives.

MONITOR TOTAL PROTEIN LEVELS

You can monitor your success in providing enough immune protection to calves by taking blood samples from calves at one to three days of age and measuring total protein. One method of estimating IgG in blood is the refractometer. This device measures the amount of light passing through a liquid sample. As light passes through the sample, it is refracted, or bent, by molecules in the liquid. In blood plasma or serum, these molecules are primarily proteins. Higher readings mean greater light refraction and more protein in the sample. IgG is only one fraction of the total protein in serum, but the two are directly related in calves up to about 48 hours of age. Measuring total protein in calves beyond 48 hours of age is less valuable because diet proteins will make up a larger fraction of the total and much of the IgG will be cleared from the blood and recycled to the intestinal tract.

If calves have received enough high quality colostrum, serum total protein will be 5.5 grams per deciliter (g/dl) or greater (1 dl is equivalent to 100 ml). When total protein falls between 5.0 and 5.5 g/dl, calves are at marginal risk of illness and death. Total serum protein levels less than 5.0 g/dl put the calf at high risk for health problems. The relationship between IgG and total protein is different in calves fed colostrum products based on bovine serum. When using a refractometer to measure the immune status of these calves, the target protein level is 4.75 g/dl.

Commercial calf-side tests offer another way to monitor passive transfer. These kits measure IgG directly and can be used with whole blood or serum. Results, which are ready in about 20 minutes, indicate either success (IgG greater than 10 mg/ml) or failure (IgG less than 10 mg/ml) of passive transfer. These kits measure actual IgG, so feeding serum-based colostrum products does not affect their result.

COMPARING MONITORING METHODS

For on-farm use, there is an initial purchase cost of a refractometer, but no additional cost per sample. It is a one-time equipment purchase that will last for many years. A centrifuge for blood samples is not required, but it does speed up the process. Alternatively, serum can be harvested by collecting blood and allowing it to stand for about 2 hours to form a clot, which allows the serum to form a separate layer at the top of the tube. Or the sample can be refrigerated overnight to allow the clot to settle at the bottom.

Other calf-side tests have a cost of $4 to $5 per sample. The whole blood kits are slightly faster because no separation is required. The plasma kits require more time than whole blood (but the same as a refractometer) and a centrifuge to separate plasma from red blood cells. Both the refractometer and the calf-side tests are accurate; the differences are in cost per sample, time required to get results and the type of results. The refractometer provides an actual value for total protein in the blood, while the calf-side kits provide a pass-fail test of whether the IgG level is above or below 10 mg/ml.

Colostrum feeding affects both illness and death rates. Calves with low IgG levels (less than 10 mg/ml) are more than twice as likely to die as calves with higher levels (Figure 1.11). Consistently feeding colostrum with high antibody levels and low bacteria counts is the foundation for raising healthy calves. Careful attention to the details of colostrum management will pay off in reduced illness and improved growth, benefits that affect the productivity of the animal for a lifetime.

FEEDING

The fascinating differences between calves and mature ruminants create unique nutritional needs for preweaned calves. At birth, the dairy calf's digestive system is underdeveloped. Unlike a cow, the calf is a monogastric, or simple-stomached, animal from birth to about 2 weeks of age. The calf's reticulum, rumen, and omasum are inactive and undeveloped. The abomasum is the only stomach compartment actively involved in digestion, and milk or milk replacer provides nutrients. As the calf begins to eat dry feeds, particularly grains containing readily fermentable carbohydrates, the rumen takes on a more important role. The size of each compartment increases as the calf grows. In the rumen, the fingerlike projections called papillae develop and grow longer, and the muscular walls thicken as the calf becomes a ruminant animal.

An overview of anatomy

At birth, the calf's stomach contains the same four compartments found in adult ruminants. However, the newborn's functional stomach, the abomasum, is similar to a human's stomach. As the calf grows and begins to consume a variety of feeds, its stomach compartments grow and change accordingly (Figure 2.1).

The abomasum constitutes 60 percent of the newborn calf's stomach capacity. In contrast, it makes up only 8 percent of the stomach capacity in a mature cow. At birth, the reticulum and rumen make up 30 percent of the stomach capacity, and the omasum makes up the remaining 10 percent. By 4 weeks of age, the reticulum and rumen comprise roughly 58 percent of the stomach, the omasum remains about the same at 12 percent, and the abomasum falls to about 30 percent. By 12 weeks of age, the reticulum and rumen will make up more than two-thirds of the total stomach capacity. The omasum still makes up about the same proportion at 10 percent. In contrast, the abomasum comprises only 20 percent. As the stomach develops more fully, the calf begins functioning as a mature ruminant. The abomasum continues to function as it did at birth and has grown in size. However, the reticulum and rumen grow in size and function, and they become the most important parts of the stomach system.

The stomach compartments grow in proportion to the calf's body size, but diet also affects the physical size of the stomach. By 4 weeks of age, calves fed only milk or milk replacer have a small rumen. As the amount of milk or milk replacer fed increases, the abomasum grows in size, but the rumen remains proportionately small and grows only moderately.

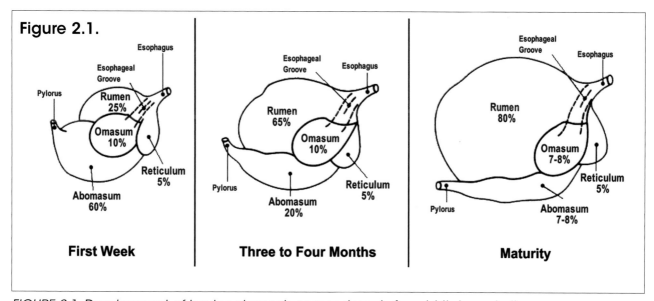

FIGURE 2.1. Development of bovine stomach compartments from birth to maturity.

This difference is especially obvious when calves of the same age fed different diets are compared. The physical size of the rumen will continue to be small in relation to the abomasum if the calf receives a diet of only milk or milk replacer for 6, 8, 12 or more weeks. The longer a calf is fed large amounts of liquid feed, the more restricted rumen growth will be relative to the size of the calf. Interestingly, while the calf appears normal, in fact she may be growing rapidly, the rumen is underdeveloped. This underdeveloped rumen will reduce growth rates after weaning.

PRE-RUMINANT DIGESTION

At birth the rumen and reticulum are nonfunctional; they have little tissue development and lack a population of microorganisms. In the absence of a functional reticulorumen, the calf depends on digestive enzymes. These are released primarily from the abomasum and small intestine and break down fats, carbohydrates, and protein. In the young calf, liquids can bypass the rumen and flow directly to the abomasum through the esophageal groove. The esophageal groove is formed when muscular folds from the reticulorumen come together, stimulated by sights and sounds calves associate with feeding and a reflexive response to swallowing. Any liquid (milk or water) consumed while the calf is excited by the anticipation of feeding bypasses the rumen and enters the abomasum. On the other hand, when the calf drinks in response to thirst, liquid enters the rumen instead of the abomasum. The esophageal groove forms whether calves are fed from a nipple bottle or from an open pail. Within 10 minutes after milk or colostrum feeding, the liquid forms a clot in the abomasum due to enzymes (chymosin and pepsin) and

hydrochloric acid acting on casein (milk protein) and fat in the milk. Chymosin, also known as rennin, binds specifically with casein. Clotting turns much of the casein and fat into a clump, or curd, to be digested slowly by stomach enzymes over a period of 12 to 18 hours.

Many of the enzymes required for normal, rapid digestion of feeds are produced in limited amounts in the first 48 hours of life. Low enzyme activity and curd formation following first colostrum feeding allow the calf to digest and absorb nutrients slowly and efficiently, which helps to prevent scours caused by undigested nutrients reaching the large intestine. When a second feeding of colostrum or transition milk occurs, it simply adds to the already-formed curd in the calf's stomach. This system allows the calf to receive a steady supply of nutrients over the first 24 to 48 hours of life, as long as it is fed casein-containing liquids. The fraction of milk that escapes curd formation is called whey. Whey is composed of water, minerals, lactose, and other proteins, including immunoglobulins or antibodies. Whey passes directly into the small intestine for absorption and/or digestion within 10 minutes after feeding. From the small intestine, immunoglobulins can be absorbed into the calf's bloodstream. Again, the newborn's limited digestive capacity is adapted to enable rapid absorption of antibodies that the calf needs.

Digestion of carbohydrates by the newborn calf is relatively poor; the exception is lactose or milk sugar. Digestion of starch varies according to its origin and processing methods. By 3 to 4 weeks of age, there is a marked improvement in the calf's ability to digest starches and vegetable proteins in feeds as enzymes become more active.

RUMEN DEVELOPMENT

From birth to about 2 weeks of age, the calf is a monogastric animal. The abomasum is the only stomach compartment actively involved in digestion, and milk or milk replacer provides nutrients. As the calf begins to eat dry feeds, particularly starter, the rumen begins to supply nutrients produced by fermentation. The most important end products of fermentation are the volatile fatty acids (VFA) butyrate, propionate and acetate. Butyrate is primarily responsible for developing rumen metabolic activities. Once the calf begins eating grain, it takes about 3 weeks to establish enough bacteria to ferment enough feed to contribute a substantial amount of energy to the calf. In addition to energy from fermentation endproducts, the establishment of a population of rumen bacteria also provides the calf with rumen microbial protein—bacteria that are washed out of the rumen, digested, and absorbed in the small intestine. This protein is highly digestible and contains a very favorable profile of amino acids. The final stage of development occurs at weaning when the rumen becomes the most important part of the digestive system, and the calf derives all energy and protein from dry feed.

The change from monogastric to ruminant requires chemical and physical changes in the calf, some of which can be aided or controlled by nutrition and management. First, bacteria must be present to carry out fermentation. Bacterial populations will increase automatically as the calf begins to eat dry feeds, but the types of bacteria present depend on the feeds eaten by the calf. For example, starter and hay promote very different bacterial populations. These microorganisms in the rumen require a liquid environment; they must have water to grow and ferment. Providing fresh, clean, free-choice water in the first few days of life will ensure a fluid rumen environment. Another factor in rumen development is the initiation of muscular contractions that move material through the rumen. Continuous flow of digested feeds is necessary to increase digestion and intake. Motility of the rumen increases automatically as calves eat more dry feed. Grains with a coarse texture are more effective in stimulating muscle growth than finely ground and pelleted grains.

WAIT TO FEED HAY

The next important factor in rumen development is absorption of fermentation products, especially VFA, which are used as energy sources for the calf. Rumen development and the ability to produce and absorb VFA must happen before weaning to avoid drastic weight loss and growth slump when calves are weaned. Absorption of VFA occurs along the rumen epithelium, with its many papillae. The papillae increase the surface area of the rumen and allow greater absorption of VFA. At birth, the papillae

are short and inactive. During rumen development, the papillae increase in size and absorptive ability. Research on the effects of different feeds on papillary development shows that fermentation of feed particles to produce VFA, especially butyrate, stimulates papillae growth and development. Research shows that chemical factors (VFA), not physical factors (forage), are the stimulus for rumen development.

For many years, producers have fed hay to pre-weaned calves based on the theory that rumen development required physical stimulation, or "scratch." Research has shown this is not the case. Furthermore, fermentation of readily available non-structural carbohydrates in calf starter results in the highest amounts of propionate and butyrate, and therefore the greatest development of ruminal epithelium. Fermentation of the complex structural carbohydrates in forage produces mostly acetate, which does not stimulate as much growth.

Intake of dry feed directly controls the availability of fer-

mentable material, or substrate, which is the driving force behind rumen development. Therefore, calves must be offered high quality, palatable calf starter beginning a few days after birth to promote early development of ruminal epithelium. As explained earlier, calf starter promotes greater development than hay because it provides more propionate and butyrate when fermented. In addition, grain is fermented more rapidly and more completely than forage, which increases the rate of passage of feedstuffs. Forage is more slowly digested and remains in the digestive tract longer, creating gut fill that prevents the calf from eating more feed. Hay also contains less energy per unit than grain. If calves eat hay instead of starter before weaning, rumen development and growth rates will be slowed down, and calves will be more likely to experience a growth slump after weaning.

However, hay does become important after weaning. Forage encourages further development of the rumen's muscular layer and prevents the build-up of keratin between papillae. Offer high qual-

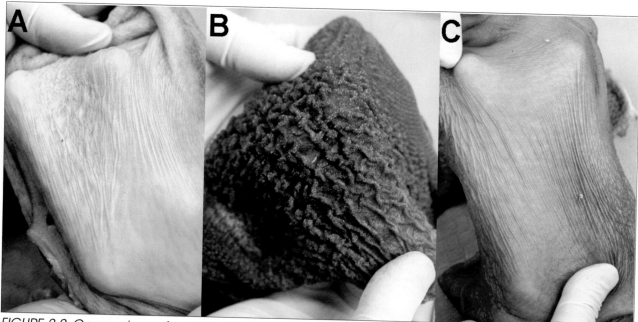

FIGURE 2.2. Comparison of rumen papillae development at 6 weeks in calves fed milk only (A), milk and grain (B) or milk and dry hay (C).

ity hay to weaned calves once grain intake reaches about 5 to 6 pounds (2.3 to 2.7 kg) daily, probably around 6 to 7 weeks of age.

The photos in Figure 2.2 clearly show the effect of different feeding strategies on rumen development. Grain is essential to increase rumen development; forage is not necessary. The photos show the rumens from three calves at 6 weeks of age. Each calf was fed a different diet: milk replacer only (A), milk replacer plus grain (B), or milk replacer plus hay (C). Grain and hay were offered beginning 3 days after birth and were consumed in moderate amounts. The calf fed grain in addition to milk has a great deal more papillae development and a much thicker, darker and more vascularized rumen wall than the other calves. In contrast, in the calf fed hay the papillae are not developed and the rumen wall is quite thin. Recall that these differences are due to the end products of digestion: hay produces mostly acetic acid, which is not used by the rumen walls and does not help the papillae grow and develop. Calves that have access to large amounts of roughage will have a considerable increase in rumen size; however this is due largely to stretching of the tissues and not real growth. In fact, the rumen development of a 4-week-old calf on milk and grain is greater than a 12-week-old calf fed milk and hay. The rumen development of calves fed milk, grain, and hay will vary from calf to calf depending on feed preferences.

From the standpoint of efficiently and economically feeding dairy replacements, developing the rumen so that it can serve as a fermentation chamber for forages and grains is fundamental. The bottom line is that a small amount of grain along with water will create fermentation and therefore butyric acid production in the rumen. This in turn allows a more functional rumen that can better digest grains, and later in life, forages. The process of rumen papillae growth is self-generating and can allow the calf fed grain early in life to have a tremendous amount of rumen development even at 3 to 4 weeks of age. Calves started on grain late or those that do not eat a substantial amount of grain early on are at a definite disadvantage in rumen development and may suffer in growth rate once they are weaned.

NUTRIENT REQUIREMENTS

Protein and energy requirements of calves fed milk and calf starter are presented in Table 2.1. Protein provides amino acids used to build body tissues. Energy is used to support body functions and allow dietary protein to be used in building body tissue. The amounts of protein and energy required by a calf are divided into two categories based on their use for maintenance and growth. Maintenance describes the amount of energy and protein needed to support normal bodily functions, including maintaining body temperature. Maintenance requirements are related to body

Table 2.1. Requirements of calves fed milk replacer* and starter**

Body weight	Calves gaining 1.0 lb (.45 kg)/day				Calves gaining 1.5 lb (.68 kg)/day			
	Energy NEm[1]	NEg[2]	ME[3]	Crude protein	Energy NEm[1]	NEg[2]	ME[3]	Crude protein
lb(kg)	Mcal	Mcal	Mcal	lb(g)	Mcal	Mcal	Mcal	lb(g)
45 (20)	0.83	0.65	2.01	0.33(150)	0.83	1.07	2.63	0.47(213)
55 (25)	0.96	0.70	2.24	0.34(154)	0.96	1.14	2.92	0.48(218)
65 (30)	1.09	0.75	2.46	0.34(154)	1.09	1.21	3.18	0.49(223)
75 (34)	1.21	0.79	2.67	0.35(159)	1.21	1.28	3.43	0.49(223)
85 (39)	1.33	0.82	2.87	0.36(163)	1.33	1.34	3.66	0.50(227)
95 (43)	1.45	0.85	3.06	0.36(163)	1.45	1.39	3.88	0.51(232)
105 (48)	1.56	0.88	3.25	0.37(168)	1.56	1.44	4.10	0.51(232)
115 (52)	1.67	0.91	3.42	0.37(168)	1.67	1.49	4.30	0.52(236)
125 (57)	1.78	0.94	3.60	0.38(173)	1.78	1.53	4.50	0.53(241)
150 (68)	2.04	1.00	4.01	0.39(177)	2.04	1.63	4.97	0.54(245)
200 (91)	2.53	1.11	4.77	0.42(191)	2.53	1.81	5.84	0.57(259)

* 60% of diet, 2.15 Mcal/lb ME; ** 40% of diet, 1.49 Mcal/lb ME
Adapted from Nutrient Requirements of Dairy Cattle, 2001.
1 NEm = net energy for maintenance.
2 NEg = net energy for gain.
3 ME = metabolizable energy.

size; bigger animals have higher maintenance needs. Environmental conditions also affect maintenance requirements. Calves housed in drafty, wet conditions have more maintenance energy needs than those housed in draft-free, dry environments. Extremely cold or hot weather also increases energy needs. Growth requirements account for the nutrients required to build body tissues. It is important to understand that nutrients the calf consumes are used to support maintenance first. Most nutrients fed in excess of maintenance needs can be used for growth. Notice in Table 2.1 that calves with the same body weight have the same energy requirements for maintenance, regardless of growth rate. Nutrients needed

to support growth logically increase as growth rate increases.

Calf growth is affected by many factors, but daily intake of protein and energy are the most important. Most often, energy intake is the first limiting factor to growth. If a calf consumes more energy than she needs for maintenance, the "extra" energy can be used to convert dietary protein into body tissue. However, if a calf consumes less energy than required for maintenance, there is no energy available for growth. Diets must provide enough energy to support growth and enough protein to be used for that growth. Feeding too little of either nutrient, or feeding the wrong ratio of energy to protein, will limit growth. Nutrients are provided by

liquid feeds and starter grain, and intake and composition of both these feeds affect growth potential. In addition, it is important to pay close attention to the day-to-day variability in liquid feeds as nutrient fluctuations can contribute to scours and poor growth in young calves.

Figure 2.3 demonstrates the difference in energy needs between calves. If calves are fed the same daily amount of metabolizable energy (ME), for example, one pound per day of milk replacer containing 20 percent protein and 20 percent fat (2.15 Mcal ME/lb or 4.75 Mcal ME/kg), you might think all calves will gain weight at the same rate. This is not the case, because calves with different body weights have different mainte-

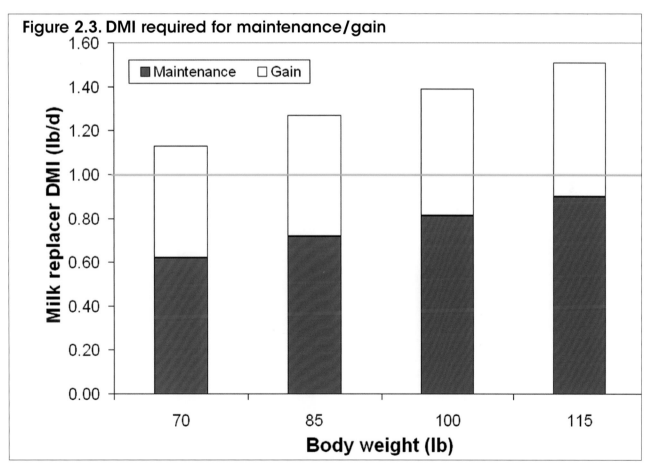

FIGURE 2.3. Dry matter intake required to meet net energy needs for maintenance (solid bars) plus one pound of gain per day (open bars) in calves fed milk replacer containing 20% protein and 20% fat (2.15 Mcal/lb ME). A line drawn at milk replacer intake of one pound per day shows that none of the calves will be able to gain one pound per day when fed only milk replacer at this rate.

nance energy requirements. A constant feeding level will meet the needs of an average calf, but exceed the needs of smaller calves and fall short of the needs of larger calves, resulting in different rates of gain. Notice that all four calves in Figure 2.3 will need more than one pound (0.45 kg) of milk replacer powder per day to achieve one pound (0.45 kg) of gain per day. In Figure 2.3, all four calves have their maintenance energy needs satisfied when fed one pound (0.45 kg) of milk replacer. Energy consumed in excess of maintenance needs can be applied to growth. Therefore, calves with greater excess energy can be expected to grow more. However, there is another factor to consider—increased growth requires increased dietary protein.

Figure 2.4 shows the increase in protein requirements as rate of gain increases. The graph also shows that calves fed high levels of protein must be fed more dry matter to realize improved rates of gain. If dry matter is not increased, the extra protein is wasted because energy becomes the first limiting factor. The nitrogen in this excess protein ends up in manure, increasing the amount of nitrogen that must be removed from the farm. In addition, the amount fed to each calf must be adjusted as the calf grows to ensure both energy and protein needs are met. Based on the requirements shown in Figure 2.4, a standard 20 percent crude protein milk replacer fed at 1.23 pounds (0.56 kg) per calf per day will support daily gains of 0.75 pound (0.34 kg) in

calves weighing 100 pounds (45.4 kg). Usually, this rate of gain is sufficient, and it is increased to over one pound (0.45 kg) per day as the calf begins to consume dry feed.

These examples not only demonstrate the relationship between energy and protein, they also reinforce the importance of knowing each calf's actual body weight. Guessing a calf's birth weight and feeding her less than she requires in the first few weeks of life may limit her growth. On the other hand, overfeeding of young or small calves could result in more digestive upsets and scours as well as lower starter intake, which restricts rumen development. Weight tapes designed specifically for calves can be used if scales are not avail-

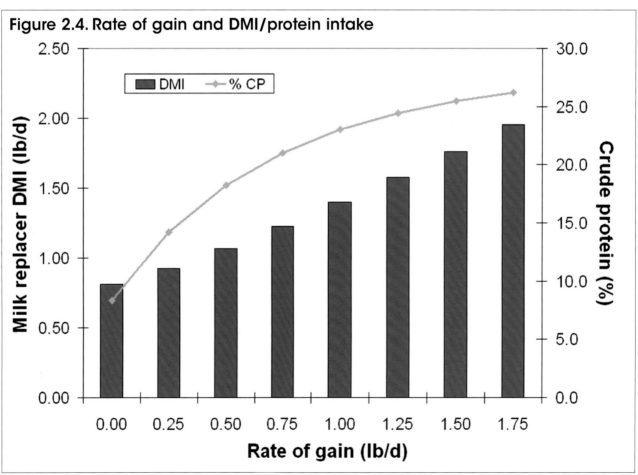

FIGURE 2.4. Relation of rate of gain and protein/dry matter intake requirements of a 100-pound calf fed 20% protein, 20% fat milk replacer containing 2.15 Mcal/lb ME.

able. Remember, to feed calves accurately, the weight of both calves and feeds must be known.

RECOMMENDED FEEDING AMOUNT

Typically, liquid feeding programs are designed to limit the amount of liquid feed and encourage early intake of dry feeds. While these programs do not support maximal weight gains before weaning, they do promote rumen development and early weaning. Early weaning systems encourage rumen development and continued growth after weaning. Calves can be fed liquid feeds at higher rates and, with proper care, have improved growth without increased rates of nutritional scours. However, differences in calf growth due to preweaning feeding rate typically disappear by the time calves reach 4 to 6 months of age. In evaluating different feeding programs, the increased cost of feed must be weighed against increased weight gain using cost per pound of gain. In addition, the long-term impact of higher rates of gain must be evaluated from an economic standpoint. Weight advantages at weaning must translate into reduced age at first calving, increased milk production, or improved health if they are to be cost effective for the majority of U.S. dairy operations.

A general recommendation is to feed milk at 10 percent of birth weight or milk replacer at 10 to 12 percent of birth weight. As an example, feeding at 12 percent of birth weight, a 100-pound (45.4-kg) calf would need 12 pounds (5.4 kg) of milk replacer per day. This amount is typically divided into two feedings of 6 pounds (2.7 kg). One pint of liquid milk or milk replacer weighs about 1 pound, so this would be 3 quarts (2.8 L) at each feeding. At 10 percent of bodyweight, a calf weighing 80 pounds (36.3 kg) would receive 8 pounds (3.6 kg), fed in two feedings of 2 quarts (1.8 L) each. Suggested feeding rates for calves are shown in Table 2.2. Faster growth rates can be achieved at higher feeding rates, but be sure to work the amount you are feeding up gradually to allow calves to adjust and to limit scouring. Growth rates over 1.75 pounds (0.79 kg) per day are not recommended for young calves before puberty. Remember, if all calves are fed the same amount regardless of body weight, some will be underfed and some will be overfed. The amount fed must be adjusted during periods of stress, including severely cold tempera-

Table 2.2. Suggested feeding rate for liquid feeds

Amount to feed each day (pounds or pints)

Birth weight (lb)	Milk Replacer[1]	Whole or Waste Milk[2]	Fermented Milk[2,3]	
			Milk	Water
40 to 50	5.4	4.5	3.0	1.5
50 to 60	6.6	5.5	3.7	1.8
60 to 70	7.8	6.5	4.3	2.2
70 to 80	9.0	7.5	5.0	2.5
80 to 90	10.2	8.5	5.7	2.8
90 to 100	11.4	9.5	6.3	3.2
100 to 110	12.6	10.5	7.0	3.5
110 to 120	13.8	11.5	7.7	3.8

1 - Fed at 12% of birth weight.
2 - Fed at 10% of birth weight.
3 - Diluted 2 parts fermented milk to 1 part water.

Amount to feed each day (liters)

Birth weight (kg)	Milk Replacer[1]	Whole or Waste Milk	Fermented Milk[2,3]	
			Milk	Water
18 to 23	2.5	2.1	1.4	0.7
23 to 27	3.1	2.6	1.7	0.9
27 to 32	3.7	3.1	2.0	1.0
32 to 36	4.2	3.5	2.4	1.2
36 to 41	4.8	4.0	2.7	1.3
41 to 45	5.4	4.5	3.0	1.5
45 to 50	5.9	4.9	3.3	1.7
50 to 55	6.5	5.4	3.6	1.8

A colored number or tag on each pen indicates individual feeding amounts, as birth weights can vary among calves.

tures, particularly for calves under 3 weeks of age. Effects of the environment on nutrient needs and feeding practices are discussed more at the end of this chapter.

Since calf birth weights can cover a rather wide range, grouping calves by weight as they are born can allow you to achieve more consistent growth rates. An example for Holstein calves would be feeding the average 80- to 90-pound (36.3- to 40.8-kg) calves the standard amount of milk replacer; calves less than 80 pounds (36.3 kg) get one-half quart (0.5 L) less milk, and those greater than 90 pounds (40.8 kg) would be fed one-half quart (0.5 L) more. A colored or numbered tag on each pen or hutch can then be used to signify the amount each calf is to be fed. In this way, all calves will gain at a more similar rate and young calves will not be overfed, which will help them avoid scouring and reduced starter intake.

CALF FEEDING SYSTEMS

Typically the calf feeding program calls for two feedings per day and each calf is fed from an individual container. However, there are alternative feeding systems that may work in some situations. One labor-saving system involves feeding calves all of their milk in a single feeding. In addition to feeding time, calves must be observed at least one other time during the day. This strategy is most likely to work when calf care is exceptional and calves have been performing well historically. Keep in mind that in general, calves seem to perform better if they are fed twice daily until the age of 2 weeks. So when milk is fed only once daily, careful attention to calf health and the supply of water and grain is essential.

Another strategy for maximizing labor efficiency is the use of group housing and feeding. Calves are kept in small groups and fed from a large tank with multiple nipples ("mob feeder") or from a computerized feeder. Under careful management group feeding systems can be successful; however, choosing to raise calves in groups will increase the risk of spreading disease between ani-

Group feeding can be successful with careful management, but it does increase the risk of disease spread.

Table 2.3. Comparison of liquid feeds for calves

Feed	Nutrient quality	Palatability	Cost	Disease risk	Storage and handling	Consistency
Milk replacer	Wide range[1]	Range[1]	Range[2]	Very Low	Very convenient	High[3]
Excess colostrum & waste milk:						
Fresh/frozen	Good	Excellent	Lowest[4]	High[5]	Most intensive[6]	Moderate[7]
Fermented	Good	Good	Lowest[4]	High[5]	Most intensive[6]	Moderate[7]
Pasteurized	Good	Excellent	Moderate	Low	Most intensive[6]	Moderate[7]
Whole milk	Excellent	Excellent	Highest	Moderate[5]	Convenient[6]	Moderate

1 - Depends on ingredients and processing.
2 - Depends on ingredients; less expensive than whole milk.
3 - If mixed properly.
4 - Potentially expensive opportunity cost.
5 - Depends on disease status of the herd.
6 - May depend on location of cows and calves.
7 - Depends on number of cows and reasons milk was discarded.

mals. Calves must be provided with adequate immunity from colostrum if they are kept in groups. In addition, maintaining clean, dry bedding and good ventilation are essential. Finally, regular cleaning of feeding equipment must occur to limit the growth of bacteria. Research shows that cross-sucking can be minimized by providing enough opportunities for calves to suck a nipple and limiting competition between calves. These opportunities can be provided by limiting the number of calves in a group to 10, minimizing size and age differences between calves, providing one nipple per calf when using a mob feeder, and restricting access to a computer feeder so only one calf can enter at a time.

Additional strategies when using a computer feeder include: diluting milk replacer with extra water, reducing the size of the nipple opening, and providing larger meals to increase the amount of suckling for each meal. To use the computer feeder each calf receives a transponder that allows the feeder to recognize individuals and dispense milk according to their programmed needs. The feeder usually can be programmed to determine the amount fed in each feeding, the number of meals each day, and the time allowed between feedings. Other settings vary by manufacturer and model. Computer feeding systems are also available for grain. Careful observation of calf health is essential to the success of group feeding; one sick calf could quickly spread her illness to all the calves in the group. It may be helpful to remove scouring calves from the group and feed them individually until they are healthy again.

LIQUID FEED OPTIONS AND ECONOMICS

After colostrum, there are generally four liquid feed choices for the pre-weaned calf: whole milk, milk replacer, excess colostrum/transition milk, or waste milk. Each of these options has advantages and disadvantages; Table 2.3 presents a summary of some considerations for choosing liquid feeds. When comparing different options consider differences in the amount of nutrients provided as well as the cost. Cost per pound of gain may be helpful in comparing feeds that differ in composition or amount fed. Cost comparisons for alternative feeding systems also may include expected differences in the rates of sickness and death and the associated costs of treatment or loss.

The value of feeds is best compared on a dry matter or "solids" basis to allow an accurate comparison of feeds with different solids content. To determine the cost of a pound of milk replacer, simply divide the price per bag by the weight in the bag. Then divide this price by the dry matter concentration of the powder. If no dry matter value is provided on the bag, an estimate of 95 percent may be used. Whole milk is valued at the price received for milk sold. Divide the price per hundredweight by 100 to calculate the price per pound of liquid. Then divide this price by the solids content of the milk, typically about 12.5 percent. The result is the value of one pound of milk solids. Transition milk and colostrum can be considered free, as they cannot be sold.

Putting a dollar value on waste milk is a little more complicated, and there are several methods used. At a minimum, the value of waste milk is equal to the cost of production. This may be a valid cost for a portion of the milk because most farms will have some waste milk. However, if the number of cows being treated is greater than 3 percent of the milking herd, then the true value of waste milk must include an opportunity cost. If cows were not being treated, this milk would have the same value as all other milk sold. Therefore, the value of waste milk may be as high as the price received for whole milk. To find the value of solids in waste milk an estimate of 12.5 percent can again be used. In addition to the milk value, if milk is pasteurized these costs must be considered as well. The pasteurizer and associated equipment for hauling or storing milk should be assigned an annual cost that includes purchase price, depreciation, installation, operation (including cleaning), and labor for the pasteurization process. This annual cost can then be spread out over the total pounds of milk pasteurized in a year. The pasteurization cost is then added to the value of milk to determine the true cost of the feed.

ALL MILK REPLACERS ARE NOT CREATED EQUALLY

A majority of dairy calves in the U.S. are fed milk replacer for most or all of their liquid feeding period. Convenience and biosecurity are key factors that make milk replacer appealing. There are many options available for calf milk replacer, and each is designed to meet different needs. To sort through them, first set goals for calf growth, health and weaning age. Then select a product designed to meet those goals. When comparing products, the first step is to read the label. The most important items to identify are the crude protein and fat content, ingredients and feeding instructions. Differences in the price of milk replacer are due to ingredient selection, manufacturing technology and nutritional quality. Consider these factors when balancing cost and calf performance.

Protein sources are the most expensive ingredients in milk replacer. As a result, manufacturers are continually searching for less expensive ingredients. The source of milk replacer protein changes in response to ingredient cost and may include a variety of milk and non-milk proteins. Milk proteins are typically more digestible and contain a more favorable profile of amino acids than non-milk proteins. Compared to milk proteins, vegetable proteins often contain more crude protein, but their amino acid content is not as desirable. Some soy-based milk replacer contains added lysine and methionine to improve the amino acid profile. Most soy isolates or concentrates used today are highly digestible to the young calf. Egg protein contains a favorable profile of amino acid acids and most products are highly digestible. Some common sources of milk replacer protein are described in the sidebar on page 32.

Recommendations for the acceptability of protein sources are presented in Table 2.4. Sources listed under "best" are milk-based.

Those described as "acceptable" are made specifically for use in calf milk replacer. Their use is well researched. Sources listed as "marginal" are sometimes used in calf milk replacer and may vary in quality. These should be used with caution since some research with these sources shows poor results. Feed an all-milk protein milk replacer for at least the first 3 weeks of life because these very young calves cannot digest non-milk proteins as efficiently as older calves. The amount of protein calves need depends on the amount of milk replacer fed, amount of calf starter they eat, energy content of milk replacer, the milk replacer protein source, and the growth rate you are trying to achieve. Generally, milk replacer contains between 20 and 28 percent crude protein; 20 to 22 percent is most common.

Energy in milk replacer is provided by fat and carbohydrates. Fat provides a very concentrated energy source (2.25 times more energy than carbohydrates); therefore, differences in milk replacer energy levels are usually due to differences in fat content. Fat levels in milk replacer typically range from 10 to 22 percent, with 15 to 20 percent most common. In the U.S. most fat in calf milk replacer comes from lard or choice white grease. These animal fats are much cheaper than milk fat and are 88 to 96 percent digestible. Plant oils from palm or coconut are also acceptable sources with digestibil-

ities of 92 to 96 percent. Typically, antioxidants to prevent rancidity and emulsifiers to improve mixability and digestibility are blended with fat sources. Energy from carbohydrates is provided by lactose (or its component sugars glucose and galactose), because lactase is the only sugar-digesting enzyme young calves produce.

In addition to protein and fat contents, balanced amounts of minerals and vitamins, which are important in cell respiration and metabolism, must be provided in milk replacer. Both major and trace minerals are supplied in milk replacer, along with vitamins A, D, and E. The pre-ruminant calf also needs supplemental B-vitamins. In older cattle the rumen microbes produce these vitamins, but young calves do not have adequate microbial vitamin synthesis. Suggested mineral and vitamin concentrations for milk replacer are presented in Table 2.5.

ACCELERATED GROWTH REPLACERS
Many companies now offer high protein, low fat milk replacer (protein greater than 24 percent and fat less than 20 percent) that provide additional protein for increased growth. It is important to pay close attention to the feeding instructions for these milk replacers. Calves must be fed more than in conventional programs and the amount fed to each calf may need to be adjusted as the calf grows. Instructions for feeding are detailed on the milk

Table 2.4. Sources of milk replacer protein

Best	Acceptable*	Marginal
Dried whey protein concentrate	Soy protein isolate	Soy flour
Dried skim milk	Protein modified soy flour	Modified potato protein
Casein	Soy protein concentrate	
Dried whey	Animal plasma	
Dried whey product	Egg protein	
	Modified wheat protein	

Adapted from A Guide to Modern Milk Replacer, Bovine Alliance on Management and Nutrition, 2002.
*Acceptable when used as a partial substitute for milk protein.

replacer feed tag. To make these feeding programs cost effective, the increased cost of high protein milk replacer and the extra cost to feed more dry matter must be offset by long-term improvements in growth or decreased overall heifer production costs, possibly including reduced age at first calving. Typically, changes to the calf feeding program alone cannot achieve these long-term cost-reduction goals; changes in the feeding and management of older calves and heifers must occur as well. Calves also must be managed more carefully when feeding for higher rates of gain as they may be more susceptible to nutritional scours, especially when milk replacer is fed at greater than 12.5 percent solids and water availability is limited. Grain intake often is reduced in early life, thereby limiting rumen development. In some cases, this can result in restricted growth after weaning and produce calves that are similar in size to conventionally fed calves by 4 to 6 months of age.

If your goal is to increase calf growth before weaning, you will get better results with one of the accelerated programs than by simply feeding more of a conventional milk replacer. Recall the relationship between protein, energy and dry matter intake discussed previously. This relationship is the reason conventional milk replacer cannot be fed at high rates without creating fat calves. It also explains why accelerated products produce disappointing results if you do not feed enough; the additional protein in the replacer is wasted because energy becomes the first limiting factor. Excess protein in the diet is then excreted, increasing the nitrogen content of manure. Also, the amounts of

Table 2.5. Composition of calf feeds, dry matter basis

Nutrient	Conventional Milk Replacer[1]	Enhanced Milk Replacer[2]	Calf Starter
Crude protein (%)	20	22 to 28.5	18
Fat (%)	20	15 to 18.5	3
ADF (%)	.	.	11.6
NDF (%)	.	.	12.8
ME (Mcal/lb)	2.15	.	1.49
Macrominerals (%)			
Calcium	1.0	0.75 to 1.0	0.7
Phosphorus	0.7	0.6 to 0.7	0.45
Magnesium	0.07		0.1
Sodium	0.4		0.15
Potassium	0.65		0.65
Chloride	0.25		0.2
Sulfur	0.29		0.2
Microminerals (ppm)			
Iron	100		50
Manganese	40		40
Zinc	40		40
Copper	10		10
Iodine	0.5		0.25
Cobalt	0.11		0.1
Selenium	0.3		0.3
Vitamins (IU/lb)			
Vitamin A	4091	7500 to 40,000	1818
Vitamin D	273	1820 to 8625	273
Vitamin E	22.7	50 to 150	11.4

Adapted from Nutrient Requirements of Dairy Cattle, 2001.
1 - Milk replacer containing 20% protein and 20% fat, fed at 1.2 lb/d. B-vitamin supplementation is required for preruminant calves: 6.5 ppm thiamin; 6.5 ppm riboflavin; 6.5 ppm pyridoxine; 13 ppm pantothenic acid; 10 ppm niacin; 0.1 ppm biotin; 0.5 ppm folic acid; 0.07 ppm B12; 1000 ppm choline.
2 - Values in this column represent the range of commercially available products. To date, no published research has determined the appropriate values for vitamins and minerals in enhanced milk replacer, and no recommendations for enhanced formulas are provided in the 2001 Nutrient Requirements of Dairy Cattle.

minerals, vitamins, and additives in these products are adjusted to account for the higher amount fed.

ADDITIVES CAN PREVENT DISEASE

Once you decide on the nutritional aspects of your milk replacer, there are a number of other optional items that can be added to the product. Two common classes of additives include lasalocid or decoquinate to prevent coccidiosis and antibiotics to aid in preventing bacterial scours. Milk-fed dairy calves often respond favorably to oral antibiotics with increased weight gains and improved feed efficiency, but antibiotics must not be used as a substitute for good management. In addition, continued public concern about the use of antibiotics in animal feed makes it likely that this option may be discontinued in the future. Remember that feeding antibiotics in milk replacer requires a withdrawal period prior to slaughter, so do not feed medicated milk replacer to bull calves intended for sale. Four medications have approval for use in calf milk replacer: oxytetracycline, oxytetracycline in combination with neomycin (OXY/NEO), decoquinate, and lasalocid. Table 2.6 provides usage levels and withdrawal times for medicated calf feeds.

A number of alternatives to antibiotics, such as probiotics (also called direct-fed microbials), yeast, oligosaccharides, and functional proteins, are now available in milk replacer. Many of these products have not been thoroughly researched, and results of research so far have been variable. Probiotics are live cultures of naturally occurring microorganisms. The most common probiotic ingredients are lactic acid-producing bacteria. In theory, probiotics can improve dry matter intake, weight gain, feed efficiency and disease resistance. Research so far suggests a modest improvement in average daily gain and feed efficiency when probiotics are fed to young calves. It seems that probiotics would be most beneficial when calves are stressed and normal bacteria populations are disrupted. Keep in mind that probiotics are living organisms; follow the instructions for storage and use products before their expiration dates. In addition, probiotic additives should not be used with medicated milk replacer because the antibiotics may kill the probiotic organisms.

Yeast is another common direct-fed microbial. *Saccharomyces cerevisiae* is the most frequently used yeast species, and may be fed live or dead. Yeast cells are rich sources of protein and B-vitamins. They also stimulate beneficial bacteria and rumen fermentation and assist in fiber digestion. A review of microbial additives concluded that adding yeast cultures to calf diets could result in no change or a modest improvement in feed intake, weight gain and feed efficiency. Performance depends on the specific conditions of each sit-

---

Common Milk Replacer Protein Sources

Dried skimmed milk—Milk fat is removed, then the remaining skim milk containing protein, lactose, and minerals is dried (34% protein).

Casein (dried milk protein, sodium caseinate)—Skim milk is coagulated to separate the protein, which is primarily casein, then protein is dried (85% protein).

Dried whey—During cheese making, liquid whey is separated from curds, then drained and dried. Contains lactalbumin proteins and is high in lactose (12% protein).

Dried whey product (delactosed whey)—A portion of the lactose in whey is removed, which results in higher levels of protein and minerals than dried whey (20 to 26% protein).

Dried whey protein concentrate (WPC)—Protein portion of whey is concentrated through ultrafiltration (34 to 80% protein).

Soy protein isolate—Isolated protein of soybean with carbohydrate fraction removed; water soluble and fiber-free (86% protein).

Soy protein concentrate (SPC)—Protein portion of soybeans concentrated by removing soluble carbohydrates. Contains fiber (67% protein).

Protein modified soy flour—A soy flour specially processed to improve digestibility and reduce allergic reactions (50% protein).

Animal plasma—Concentrated protein source obtained by removing red and white blood cells from fresh, whole blood. The resulting plasma is dried (78% protein).

Egg protein—Spray dried whole egg or a combination of whole egg and egg albumin. Whole egg contains high fat levels (54% protein).

Modified wheat protein—Gluten protein is separated from flour then treated to increase protein solubility (80% protein).

Soy flour—Finely ground soybean meal (50% protein).

Modified potato protein—Potatoes are grated and starch extracted for use in food products. During this process, water is removed to isolate the starch. Protein is separated from this water and dried (80% protein).

uation. However, yeast cultures do tend to increase microbial growth in the rumen, which may have benefits in promoting rumen development. One California study reported that adding live yeast to milk replacer fed to calves with failure of passive transfer did not affect average daily gain. However, calves fed yeast did have fewer days with scours than control calves.

A final type of antibiotic alternative is a group of proteins known as functional proteins. Nutritionists typically think of protein in feeds as a source of amino acids, but functional proteins provide more than that. These proteins can cause a physiologic response in the body. Some are able to survive the rumen environment intact, others are released during digestion. The methods used to collect and process proteins can affect their function, so it is important to determine the viability of proteins when comparing products.

The most well-known of the functional proteins are the immunoglobulins, or antibodies. Research has shown that immunoglobulins (Ig) from the blood are recycled into the intestine. This means that providing Ig in colostrum or injecting Ig into the blood can help to boost immunity in calves. Both of these methods have been researched and found effective. In addition, plasma protein fed in milk replacer may provide antibodies that enhance the immune system locally in the intestine.

Research with plasma protein indicates that calves under stress

Prebiotics

Another category of additives is the prebiotics, which are structural carbohydrates that cannot be digested by ruminants, but are excellent nutrient sources for beneficial bacteria in the calf's digestive tract. Examples include resistant starches, polysaccharides, pectins, and gums. The mode of action varies for different types of prebiotics. One common prebiotic in calf feeds is mannanoligosaccharide (MOS), a complex sugar isolated from the cell wall of yeast. Some pathogens, including E. coil and Salmonella, will readily bind to mannan and preferentially bind to it rather than the intestinal wall. However, MOS is a form of mannan that these pathogens cannot digest. Once they bind to MOS, the bacteria cannot detach themselves, so they are passed out of the body with other undigested feedstuffs. In addition, beneficial bacteria in the intestine may utilize MOS. A Penn State study compared three milk replacers containing MOS, antibiotic (OXY/NEO), or no additive. Researchers found that calves fed MOS or antibiotic had more normal fecal scores than control calves. Calves fed MOS ate more than calves fed antibiotics, but no differences in growth were seen during the 6-week trial.

Fructooligosaccharide (FOS), another available prebiotic, is a sugar extracted from the chicory plant that selectively nourishes beneficial bacteria in the large intestine. One study showed that calves fed a product containing FOS, allicin (an extract of garlic), and probiotic cultures and calves fed antibiotic had similar fecal scores. However, no calves in this study were fed control milk replacer (with no additive), so it is impossible to determine if fecal scores were improved compared to calves that were not treated. Tennessee researchers compared calves fed galactosyl-lactose, an oligosaccharide derived from whey, antibiotic (OXY/NEO), or no additive. In this study, calves fed galactosyl-lactose or antibiotics were similar and tended to have more normal fecal scores and fewer days scouring than control calves. In addition, calves fed galactosyl-lactose gained more weight than control calves. Although results so far are promising, peer-reviewed research into oligosaccharides is scarce at this time, and additional research is needed to support growth promotion claims.

benefit from these additional antibodies, while healthy, non-stressed calves usually do not benefit. Lactoferrin is another type of functional protein. It binds to iron, making it unavailable to bacteria that need it. Lactoferrin has been shown to limit the growth of *E. coli* and rotavirus, however research with lactoferrin in milk replacer is limited and lactoferrin is an expensive additive.

EVALUATING MILK REPLACER QUALITY

Dry powder should be cream to light tan in color and free of lumps and foreign material. Powder should have a bland to pleasant odor. An orange to orange-brown color and a burned or caramelized smell indicate excessive heating during storage. Such powder will be less palatable and have lower nutrient availability. Paint, grass, clay or petroleum odors indicate possible rancidity. Once mixed into solution, liquid milk replacer should be cream to light tan in color and have a pleasant odor and milky flavor. Milk replacer supplemented with organic acids will have a tangy taste, not to be confused with the lactic acid taste of sour milk. To maintain the quality of milk replacer, store opened bags in airtight containers that keep out dust, rodents and pets. A 20-gallon (76-liter) plastic garbage can with a tight-fitting lid works well for 50-pound (23 kg) bags.

Crude fiber content and clotting, two older tests of milk replacer quality, are no longer valid methods of evaluating milk replacer. Milk protein contains no fiber, and in the past crude fiber levels above 0.2 percent were considered evidence of a plant protein source. However, highly processed soy protein can contain little to no fiber and other non-milk

Table 2.6. Antibiotics and coccidiostats in calf feeds approved by FDA

Medication	Feeding rate, mg/lb BW (g/ton of milk replacer)[1]	Label statement	Withdrawal[2]
Milk replacer only			
Oxytetracycline	0.05 to 0.1 mg/lb (10 to 20 g)	Increased rate of weight gain and improved feed efficiency	None
Oxytetracycline	10 mg/lb (2000 g)	Treatment of bacterial enteritis caused by E. coli susceptible to oxytetracycline. Feed continuously for 7 to 14 days.	5 days
Oxytetracycline and Neomycin	Oxy: 100 g Neo: 200 g	Aid in prevention of bacterial diarrhea	30 days
Oxytetracycline and Neomycin	Oxy: 200 to 400 g Neo: 400 to 800 g	Aid in treatment of bacterial diarrhea	30 days
Milk replacer or calf starter			
Decoquinate	0.227 mg/lb (45.4 g)	For prevention of coccidiosis in ruminating and nonruminating calves and cattle caused by E. bovis and E. zuernii	None
Lasalocid	0.45 mg/lb (90 g)	For control of coccidiosis caused by E. bovis and E. zuernii in replacement calves	None
Calf starter only			
Monensin	0.14 to 1.0 mg/lb[3] (not approved)	For prevention and control of coccidiosis due to E. bovis and E. zuernii	None

United States Food and Drug Administration Approved Animal Drug Products (www.fda.gov/cvm/greenbook.html), current as of November 22, 2005.
1 - Daily feeding rate in mg/lb of body weight, value in parentheses indicates milk replacer concentration, g/ton of dry powder.
2 - Withdrawal period required before slaughter.
3 - Rate depends on severity of challenge; not to exceed 200 mg/animal daily.

sources like plasma and egg contain no fiber. Also, it is very difficult to accurately detect crude fiber at the low levels found in milk replacer. The rennet-clotting test identifies the amount of casein in milk replacer; a soft clot indicates more than 15 percent of the protein is casein, a firm clot means that more than 50 percent of the protein is casein. However, most modern milk replacer is based on whey protein, which does not clot when mixed with rennet. Whey protein has been fully researched and is an excellent source of protein for calves. Therefore, failure to form a clot does not indicate poor protein quality in milk replacer; it does show that casein is not present.

MIXING MILK REPLACER

Follow the manufacturer's instructions for powder and water amounts, water temperature, and mix order; these instructions typically are printed on the label. Water temperatures of 110°F (43°C) are commonly recommended. Mixing is difficult at lower temperatures, and higher temperatures can cause the fat to separate. It is important to measure dried milk replacer and water accurately to be sure the amount of solids fed is correct. Use the plastic cup provided by the manufacturer to weigh the amount of powder in one scoop. It is sometimes necessary to use less than a full cup to follow the feeding directions provided on the bag. Mix milk replacer with a wire whisk using a slow, circular motion. Whipping, mixing too fast, and mixing too long can cause foaming or separation of fat into a greasy surface layer. Good milk replacer will go into solution easily and leave no clumps of powder. Most milk replacer will settle if left standing more than 10 to 15 minutes. If milk replacer must stand before feeding, give it a quick mix with the wire whisk before feeding each calf.

FEEDING WHOLE MILK

Before the mid-1950s, whole milk was the primary liquid feed for calves. According to a survey in the early 1990s, about one-third of U.S. dairy farms still used whole milk. Even though whole milk is an excellent feed that supports very adequate weight gains and health, it is the most expensive liquid feed. If milk were not fed to calves, it would be sold at market value. Other liquid feeds are available that cost less, yet support adequate weight gain and health in calves. In addition to cost, disease transmission is a potential problem when feeding whole milk (refer to sidebar on page 16 – first section); consider pasteurizing whole milk before feeding.

FEEDING EXCESS COLOSTRUM OR TRANSITION MILK

Typically, cows make more colostrum than needed to feed their calves. Excess high quality first colostrum (containing more than 50 grams of IgG per liter) should be frozen and saved for other newborns. Lower quality colostrum should not be fed to newborns, but can be fed to calves over 2 days of age. After the first milking, milk composition progressively becomes more "normal". During this transition period, milk must be withheld from the bulk tank. Rather than pour it down the drain, many producers feed transition milk to calves. Excess colostrum and transition milk provide a high quality, economical liquid diet; however, nutrient content may vary considerably from day to day and may contribute to scouring and poor growth. This is especially true when waste milk is collected from a small number of cows. Variability in nutrient content is reduced when milk from a larger number of cows is pooled; however the risk of disease transfer increases with pooled milk. To minimize disease risk, pooled milk can be pasteurized or calves can be fed milk from a single cow.

Larger dairies may refrigerate transition milk in small bulk tanks to prevent microbial growth for a few days. Another storage option is freezing, which is similar to freezing colostrum. Single-feeding quantities stored in plastic bags or bottles and thawed daily (in warm water or on low power in a microwave) work best. Refrigeration or freezing preserves nutrients and provides an excellent quality feed with more total solids than whole milk. However, the labor and storage requirements for transition milk are large and can be prohibitive.

Excess colostrum or transition

Table 2.7. Characteristics of colostrum fermented at ambient temperature

Fermentation type	pH	Total solids, %	Crude protein, %	Fat, %
Natural	4.1 - 4.8	13.1 - 17.2	4.5 - 6.8	3.8 - 7.2
Acid treatment	4.1 - 4.8	13.5 - 17.7	4.3 - 6.8	3.6 - 5.3

Review of 18 feeding trials
Source: Foley and Otterby, 1978. Journal of Dairy Science 61:1033-1060

milk also may be stored at ambient temperatures and allowed to ferment naturally or with chemical treatment. Storage at ambient temperatures ranging from 60 to 80°F (15 to 25°C) produces acceptable feed. Cooler temperatures inhibit fermentation, while warmer temperatures allow rapid fermentation that often produces unacceptable putrid odors, as some of the proteins begin to break down. Chemical preservatives such as acetic or propionic acid can be added to slow this process. Fermentation decreases the total solids and nutrient content as bacteria convert existing nutrients into lactic acid, as well as smaller amounts of acetic, butyric and propionic acids. As acids build up, pH drops to about 4.5, and protein, fat, and lactose decline (Table 2.7). Feed soured milk within a few weeks to maximize nutrient content. See the sidebar for a summary of recommendations concerning fermented milk.

In experimental trials, calves fed fermented colostrum exhibited similar growth rates and incidence of diarrhea as those fed whole milk. Feeding fermented milk should not increase cases of clinical disease due to Salmonella or *E. coli*, especially when calves received adequate colostrum at birth. However, bacteria numbers increase rapidly for 4 to 7 days after storage. This is followed by a drop in bacteria numbers due to the acidic environment created by fermentation. Every effort must be made to prevent bacterial contamination from the time milk is collected to when it is fed. Mastitic or antibiotic waste milk may be added to stores of fermented milk. Milk collected at the first and second milking after treatment does not ferment well due to high levels of antibiotics, but later milkings do not interfere with fermentation. Fermentation may break

Recommendations for using fermented milk

- *Prevent contamination.*
- *Store at 60 to 80°F (16 to 27°C) away from direct sunlight.*
- *Use 20-gallon plastic garbage cans as storage containers; metal may corrode.*
- *Tight fitting lids prevent contamination from flies, rats, or cats.*
- *Plastic bags can be used as liners to make cleanup easier.*
- *Manage fermentation with a three-barrel system: Fill the first barrel over 2 to 3 days, and feed it within 30 days. While feeding from the first barrel, store in the second and fill the third.*
- *Stir milk prior to feeding to mix curds, whey and fat.*
- *Feed colostrum within 14 to 30 days to minimize nutrient losses and strong odors.*
- *Bloody milk should not be fermented; it may speed protein breakdown and putrid odors.*
- *Add preservatives to aid fermentation during warm temperatures. Follow manufacturers' directions on commercial preparations. Add propionic acid at 1 percent or acetic acid at 0.7 percent of milk weight.*
- *Unfermented milk can be added to fermented milk without changing nutrient composition. Chemicals should be added to each batch of new milk before it is added to storage containers, rather than waiting to treat the entire container when it becomes full. This prevents initiation of undesirable fermentation in the storage container.*

down antibiotics so calves receive lower levels than in fresh waste milk. Pooling antibiotic milk with other waste and transition milk also dilutes the antibiotics received in an individual feeding.

Transition milk contains more solids than whole milk, but it can be diluted to approximate the solids content of whole milk and fed at the same rate. Add two parts transition milk to one part warm or hot water if milk is from the second or third milking. Transition milk collected from all milkings can be diluted 3:1 since it contains fewer solids.

CAN I FEED WASTE MILK TO MY CALVES?

A USDA survey of management practices in the United States found that 87 percent of producers fed unsaleable milk from fresh cows and/or antibiotic or mastitic milk to calves for part of the liquid feeding period. Waste milk can support weight gains similar to whole milk without increasing scours or illness. However, feeding waste milk increases risks of pathogen exposure, antibiotic residues and antibiotic resistance. In addition, day-to-day variability of waste milk may contribute to scours and poor growth in young calves. See the sidebar on the next page for a summary of waste milk feeding recommendations.

Obviously, there is a high risk that waste milk contains antibiotic residues; otherwise it could be sold and there would be no waste milk. In a California study about 60 percent of waste milk samples contained antibiotics. It is unclear whether antibiotic residues in milk lead to antibiotic resistance in calves, but it is possible that bacteria will become resistant to commonly used antibiotics, making treatment of diseases (both calfhood and adult) much more difficult. A group of researchers from

Recommendations for feeding waste milk

- Consider pasteurization.
- Do not dilute waste milk. It contains about the same solids as whole milk.
- Feed at 10 to 12% of body weight each day.
- Prevent excess growth of bacteria; do not let waste milk sit at room temperature.
- Do not feed milk from cows with known infections of Johne's, BVD, Salmonella, E. coli, Pasteurella, Mycoplasma, or leukosis.
- Do not feed to group housed calves.
- Do not feed to market calves (higher risk of antibiotic residues). Wait at least 8 to 12 weeks after ending waste milk feeding before selling calves.
- Discard milk from first two milkings after antibiotic treatment.
- Do not feed excessively bloody or abnormal milk.
- Do not feed mastitic colostrum to newborns.

Canada added penicillin to milk and then fed the milk to calves 3 days per week for 5 weeks. Calves were allowed to eat as much milk as they wanted and consumed up to 23 pounds per day. Although the amount of milk fed was much higher than what most U.S. dairy calves are fed, the number of bacteria resistant to penicillin increased as the amount of penicillin in the milk increased. Increased numbers of resistant bacteria could be due to development of resistance or increased growth of resistant bacteria that were already present in the intestine. The highest concentration of penicillin was determined by sampling cows after treatment for mastitis, so this study suggests that milk from the first and possibly second milking after treatment should not be fed to calves to reduce the risk of increasing antibiotic resistance.

Feeding milk from cows treated with antibiotics can result in antibiotic residues in the calf's muscle tissue. Therefore, only feed milk from treated cows to calves kept as herd replacements or kept for 8 to 12 weeks after the last feeding of treated milk. Do not feed milk that may contain antibiotics to calves raised for bob or heavy veal. Calves also may suffer from changes in the normal population of intestinal bacteria when fed milk containing antibiotic residues. Furthermore, antibiotic residues and resistance are public health issues due to the risk of allergic reactions and the development of antibiotic-resistant human pathogens.

WASTE MILK HAS MORE MICROBIAL LIFE

California researchers sampled milk fed to calves and found significantly more live bacteria in waste milk samples than in colostrum, milk replacer, or whole milk. Species detected included Streptococcus (51 percent of samples), Enterobacteriacea (50 percent of samples), and Staphylococcus (41 percent of samples). E. coli was the most common individual organism, appearing in 32 percent of samples. No Salmonella or Mycoplasma species were detected. The microbial load of any milk increases during storage, especially at warm temperatures. However, since waste milk initially contains more microbial life than other liquid feeds, extra care in storing and handling this milk is necessary. Contamination from dirty storage containers, feeding equipment, flies, or manure increases microbial load even more. Feed milk immediately or cool it to less than 40°F (4.5°C) to inhibit bacterial growth. Pooling milk from several cows is a common, but very risky, practice. The high number of bacteria in waste milk greatly increases the chance of spreading disease, and a single infected cow could pass disease to many calves. So while pooling waste milk may dilute microbial numbers, it is not recommended unless milk is pasteurized before feeding.

Although most mastitis-causing bacteria are not transmitted from the gut to the udder inside the calf's body, these organisms can be spread by direct contact. Calves housed in groups commonly suckle one another and may spread bacteria from their mouths to the developing udder and teats of other calves, contributing to future mastitis infections. For this reason, waste milk should not be fed to group-housed calves. Some organisms, including Mycobacterium avium subspecies paratuberculosis (MAP), bovine viral diarrhea virus, and bovine leukosis virus are spread through milk. Feeding milk containing E. coli, Salmonella, and Pasteurella organisms can result in digestive or respiratory infections in calves. In addition, feeding waste milk containing Mycoplasma species has been associated with pneumonia, ear infections and arthritis in calves. Therefore, milk from cows with known infections should not be fed to calves unless it is adequately pasteurized. Be aware that although most bacteria are killed by pasteurization, some bacteria produce endotoxins that survive the process and may cause illness in calves.

PASTEURIZATION LIMITS RISK

Waste milk can be a nutritious, cost-effective feed for young calves. However, if it is fed regularly, pasteurization seriously should be considered. Pasteurization reduces microbial load by heating milk to temperatures that kill many organisms, including Staphylococcus species, Streptococcus species, E. coli, Salmonella species, bovine viral diarrhea virus, bovine leukosis virus, MAP, Mycoplasma species, and Listeria monocytogenes. Commercially-available equipment using both batch and high-temperature, short-time (HTST) pasteurization methods effectively killed MAP according to research at the USDA National Animal Disease Center. Other research has concluded that pasteurization is incapable of destroying MAP; however, most of this work was simulated with lab-scale equipment and much higher levels of bacteria than those normally found in milk. Usually, shedding of MAP in milk is minimal; however, fecal contamination of milk presents a serious risk to young calves.

Successful pasteurization requires heating to the desired temperature, maintenance of that temperature for a specific time, and rapid cooling of milk after heat treatment. Batch pasteurization requires heating milk to 145°F (63°C) and holding it for 30 minutes. Using continuous flow (HTST) pasteurization, milk must be heated to 161°F (72°C) and held for 15 seconds. Regular monitoring of the time required to achieve the target temperature, the holding time, and temperatures throughout the pasteurization and cleaning cycles are recommended for best results. In addition, check the bacteria numbers in milk before and after pasteurization to be sure your procedures remain consistent and effective. Keep in mind that pasteurization is not

---

Recommendations to pasteurize waste milk

- *Monitor pasteurization temperature and holding time for every batch of milk.*
- *Clean pasteurizer after every use following procedure recommended by the manufacturer.*
- *Periodically check bacteria numbers in milk before and after pasteurization to ensure equipment is working.*
- *After pasteurizing milk, feed it or cool it to 40°F (4.5°C) to reduce bacterial growth. Do not store at room temperature.*
- *If milk is not fed within 24 hours of pasteurization, pasteurize it again before feeding.*
- *Prevent contamination. Although pasteurization reduces bacteria numbers, it does not completely eliminate them.*

---

sterilization—some bacteria may survive. In addition, proper cleaning and sanitation of equipment and proper handling of pasteurized milk are still required to prevent excessive bacterial growth. Feed milk soon after pasteurizing and store any leftover milk at less than 40°F (4.5°C). Milk not fed within 24 hours should be pasteurized again before feeding. Herds that want to eliminate Johne's or other diseases that can be spread in milk must feed pasteurized milk. A summary of recommendations for pasteurizing waste milk appears in the sidebar.

California research found that calves fed pasteurized milk had fewer cases of diarrhea and pneumonia and higher growth rates than calves fed milk that was not pasteurized. Researchers calculated that these calves were worth $8.13 more than their herdmates when all costs and benefits were considered. The study reported that 315 calves per day were needed to justify the cost of pasteurizing milk. A Minnesota study compared pasteurized waste milk to conventional (20 percent fat, 20 percent protein) milk replacer. Feeding pasteurized milk saved $34 per calf from birth to weaning and required 23 calves per day to justify the cost. Calves fed pasteurized milk gained more weight (0.26 pounds or 0.12 kg) per day

and experienced less illness and death than calves fed milk replacer. Differences between groups were attributed mainly to the higher protein and energy content of milk compared to milk replacer.

Two studies comparing calves fed pasteurized versus non-pasteurized milk (California) or pasteurized milk versus milk replacer (Minnesota) showed lower health costs for calves fed the pasteurized milk, as well as better weight gain. There was considerable variation in the results, with the Minnesota study showing much greater advantage in health costs compared to the California study. For this reason, the Minnesota study could show a cost advantage to pasteurization with only 23 calves; the California research reported that 315 calves fed per day could justify the cost of pasteurizing milk.

Before investing in a pasteurizer, there are several important considerations that must be addressed. Determine hot water needs; some pasteurizers include a water heater while others require an external supply. In addition, the supply must provide enough volume and must reach very high temperatures. Investigate the requirements for installation including electrical needs, provision for drainage and disposal of water after cleaning, and regulations concerning the location of the pasteurizer. For instance, milk house installation of a waste milk pasteurizer may not be permitted. Handling and storage of milk before and after pasteurization must be planned. Training of employees that will use the unit and the impact on labor and time requirements also must be considered. Finally, develop estimates of waste milk volume and a plan for feeding calves when waste milk is not available.

QUALITY CONTROL

If calf health and growth are consistently poor despite adequate feeding amounts and environmental conditions, consider monitoring bacteria levels in feed "as fed." Take a sample of liquid feeds just before they are offered to calves for 3 to 5 consecutive days. Store samples in the freezer until they are all collected; then work with your veterinarian to evaluate them. Culture techniques can be used to determine the amount of bacterial contamination and the species involved. In problem situations, environmental bacteria can multiply very rapidly in liquid feeds.

Often the problem can be found in sanitation procedures for feeding equipment or the time and temperature at which milk is stored. Pasteurizers add another potential source of bacterial contamination if they are not properly cleaned, and the high temperatures create different sanitation challenges than those encountered with bottles and buckets. Be sure the manufacturer provides clear instructions for cleaning the system, and follow the prescribed procedures. Ensure that time and temperature requirements during pasteurization and cleaning are met by using a recording thermometer. The effectiveness of pasteurization also can be monitored by the alkaline phosphatase test.

Alkaline phosphatase is an enzyme naturally present in raw milk that is inactivated by pasteurization.

CALF STARTER COMPOSITION AND QUALITY

The key factor in stimulating rumen development that is essential for successful weaning is early, adequate intake of dry grain. In addition, grain feeding supplements the nutrients obtained from the calf's liquid diet, which increases the nutrients available to maintain body temperature, support the immune system, and enable greater growth. Offer a dry grain mix by 3 days of age so calves will begin to eat it as soon as possible. During the first week of life, calves eat very little grain, but by the second week, they should be eating noticeable amounts.

Most calf starters are based on corn and soybean meal due to their availability and relatively low cost. Other energy sources including barley and oats also are used; oats have the added benefit of providing a source of fiber. In addition to oats, finely chopped hay, cottonseed or soy hulls, wheat midds, wheat bran, beet pulp and dried brewer's grains are used as fiber sources. Particle size of grains and fiber sources in calf starter is important in maintaining intake and rumen papillae structure. Addition of fat to calf starters to increase starter energy value is not recommended as it will actually depress feed intake if fat is in excess of 5 percent of total dry matter. In addition to soybean meal, other sources of protein include cottonseed, canola or linseed meal. Urea and other nonprotein nitrogen sources are not recommended for calves less than 3 months of age.

Table 2.5 on page 31 shows the nutrient composition of an appropriate starter based on current

National Research Council (NRC) recommendations. The most important nutrients to evaluate are protein and fiber. Research shows that calf starter containing 18 percent crude protein on a dry matter basis is adequate to support growth in young calves, including calves on enhanced feeding programs. Other research supports a maximum protein level of about 19 percent of dry matter; levels beyond this result in greater excretion of excess nitrogen.

Starter containing acid detergent fiber (ADF) in the range of 6 to 20 percent of dry matter and neutral detergent fiber (NDF) at 15 to 25 percent of dry matter is preferred. Metabolizable energy (ME) concentration of approximately 1.5 Mcal/lb is recommended. Since young calves do not have fully developed rumens, B-vitamins may be added to starters to supplement ruminal production. These supplements may also be added to milk replacer, and B-vitamins are naturally present in milk. Be sure to consider all feed sources when calculating vitamin needs of calves.

Dry matter intake can vary quite a lot from calf to calf and from day to day for the same calf. As a result, looking at nutrient requirements on a percentage basis can be misleading. Keep in mind that calves require a certain amount of each nutrient each day, not a specific percentage. Similar to balancing rations for milking cows, the amount the calf eats directly influences the nutrient requirement expressed as a percentage of ration dry matter.

Calf starter must be palatable to encourage intake, and it commonly contains molasses or other flavor ingredients to improve palatability and reduce separation and waste. Molasses may be included in pellets or sprayed on a textured feed. There is no benefit to increasing the amount of molasses in calf starter above 5 to 6 percent of dry matter. The amount of molasses in starter influences handling as well; too much causes feed to stick together in hard "bricks", especially in cold weather.

Texture is another important factor in palatability, as calves prefer textured feed to ground meals. Textured feeds may include pellets and whole or processed grains. Dry matter intake improves when starter contains whole or roasted-rolled corn compared ground or steam-flaked corn. In addition, grain processing may influence rumen development. Papillae length and rumen wall thickness were greater in 4-week-old calves fed starter containing steam-flaked corn compared to those fed roasted-rolled and whole corn when these corn supplements made up one-third of the calf starter. However, the authors prefer roasted-rolled corn because calves eat more and experience lower acid production in the rumen following a large meal of grain. Lightly rolled grain also is more palatable than ground or steam-flaked grain, and both ground and steam-flaked are more prone to dryness and dustiness.

High-moisture grains are not recommended for young calves, since they heat quickly and often mold in feed buckets or mangers. Powdery or dusty feeds are not acceptable to calves and can lower intake and performance; this includes poorly formed pellets that produce lots of fines. Regardless of its form (pelleted or coarse grain mixture), calf starter should not be dry, dusty, moldy, or have an off-flavor. Research from California and Pennsylvania showed that calves may benefit from yeast culture in starter. In both studies, grain intake and average daily gain increased in calves fed yeast.

Calf starter often contains a coccidiostat, such as decoquinate, lasalocid or monensin. These are added to control coccidiosis, a common infection of young cattle. Coccidiosis is caused by internal parasites (Eimeria species) that damage intestinal cells and reduce their ability to absorb nutrients. Calves affected by coccidiosis exhibit diarrhea, loss of appetite, weight loss and death in some cases. Unfortunately, coccidia can cause severe intestinal damage before calves show any signs of illness, and many calves with subclinical infections never appear sick. It has been estimated that less than 5 percent of calves show clinical signs of coccidiosis, yet over 90 percent have subclinical infections. Feeding a coccidiostat can prevent coccidiosis. Including a coccidiostat is effective, easy and relatively inexpensive: make it a standard practice. If calves are switched from one coccidiostat to another, clinical cases of coccidiosis may occur. This is usually a temporary problem caused by the fact that different medications act on different stages of the coccidia life cycle. Lasalocid and monensin have the added benefit of being ionophores as well as coccidiostats; they increase feed efficiency and improve weight gains (Table 2.6, page 34).

Calves must eat enough starter to get the intended daily dosage of a coccidiostat. This amount is often 2 to 3 pounds (0.9 to 1.4 kg), which can be a problem in young or sick calves with low starter intake. For example, a required 0.3 mg/lb of body weight would equal 30 mg of the coccidiostat for a 100-lb. calf. If the starter contains 15 mg/lb, then the calf must consume 2 lbs. of starter to achieve adequate intake of the coccidiostat.

Inadequate dosage leaves calves at greater risk. High concentrations of coccidiostats, which would balance out low intakes, can reduce acceptability and palatability of starter. Starter must be managed to maintain intakes at a level that will provide the expected dose of coccidiostat. If you also feed coccidiostat in milk replacer, remember to include this amount when calculating the intake required to achieve a certain dosage.

Remove uneaten starter and clean out wet or moldy feed daily to maintain freshness and maximize intake by calves.

Starter intake also is influenced by milk feeding and water availability. High rates of milk or milk replacer feeding and high levels of fat in milk replacer depress starter intake. On the other hand, availability of fresh, clean water promotes starter intake. Freshness of starter is important as well. Offer only small handfuls at each feeding until calves begin to eat starter. Remove uneaten starter and clean out wet or moldy feed daily to maintain freshness.

WATER: THE FORGOTTEN NUTRIENT

Water makes up 70 to 75 percent of a calf's body weight and is an essential nutrient. In fact, the daily requirement for water is greater than for any other nutrient. Water transports nutrients throughout the body and is involved in every aspect of the calf's metabolism. Water also is needed to regulate body temperature and eliminate wastes. Rumen microorganisms require water to carry out fermentation; without it, rumen microbes do not grow, and VFA are not produced. In the young calf, this slows rumen development. Water also aids rumen development by diluting any VFA produced by the rumen, encouraging bacteria to continue producing additional VFA.

In young calves, water is particularly important for achieving early consumption of dry feed. Calves offered free choice water gained more weight, ate more calf starter, and had fewer scour days compared to calves receiving no water, according to Purina research on calves from birth to 4 weeks of age. Calves in the study drank about 4 pounds (1.8 kg) of water for every pound (0.45 kg) of dry matter intake. Feeding milk or milk replacer is not a substitute for water. Most water in the rumen comes from free choice water, not from liquid feeds. Therefore, calves require water over and above what is received from milk or milk replacer. It should be available free choice at all times, and it should be fresh, clean, and of good quality. In addition, there is some evidence to suggest that a divider between or physical separation of the starter and water buckets improves intake of both and enhances growth. Common problems in managing water for calves are not making water available, allowing contamination with feed or feces, and freezing. General needs for water are in Table 2.8, and guidelines for water quality are presented in Table 2.9.

ENVIRONMENTAL EFFECTS ON FEED REQUIREMENTS

Calves attempt to maintain a constant body temperature regardless of the outside temperature. Within a certain temperature range called the thermo-neutral zone (TNZ), calves can maintain body temperature without expending extra energy. Outside of this range the calf experiences stress and must use energy to maintain body temperature (Figure 2.6). The boundaries of the TNZ are not constant. They are affected greatly by the effective ambient temperature experienced

Table 2.8. Water needs for calves

Age, Mos.	Water per day
1	1.3 to 2 gal 5 to 7.6 L
2	1.5 to 2 gal 5.7 to 7.6 L
3	2.1 to 2.8 gal 8 to 10.6 L
4	3 to 3.5 gal 11 to 13 L

Calves need about half a gallon (2 L) for every pound of dry matter they eat to convert feed efficiently into weight gain.

Table 2.9. Water quality guidelines for calves

Item	Max mg/L[a]
Aluminum	0.5
Arsenic	0.05
Boron	5.0
Cadmium	0.005
Calcium[b]	500
Chloride[b]	250
Chromium	0.1
Cobalt	1.0
Copper	1.0
Fluoride	2.0
Iron[b]	0.3
Lead	0.015
Magnesium[b]	125
Manganese	0.05
Mercury	0.01
Nickel	0.25
Nitrate-nitrogen[c]	10
Nitrite-nitrogen[d]	1.0
Selenium	0.05
Sodium[e]	50
Sulfate	500
Vanadium	0.1
Zinc	5.0
Total dissolved solids[f]	<500
Total soluble salts[g]	<1000
pH[f]	7 to 9
Total bacteria[b]	<200/mL
Coliform bacteria[f]	0/100 mL

a - Unless otherwise indicated values are mg/L and are published in Nutrient Requirements of Dairy Cattle, 2001 (mg/L = ppm).
b - Dairy Reference Manual, 1995.
c - 10 mg/L safe; >20 increased risk; >40 risk death.
d - EPA Standards for Drinking Water, 2001.
e - Socha et al., 2002.
f - Beede, 2005.
g - <1000 mg/L safe; >3000 increased risk; >5000 not safe for pregnant or lactating animals.

by the calf, and are not determined solely by the outside temperature. The effective temperature depends on wind, moisture, hair coat, sunlight, bedding and rumination. Each of these factors affects temperature regulation, and the impact may differ in summer and winter.

The concern during winter is cold stress—when the temperature drops below the lower critical temperature, or LCT, calves must use energy to support basic bodily functions and maintain their body temperature. The LCT is affected by the age and size of calves. Newborn calves cannot withstand temperatures as low as month-old calves. Small calves have a larger surface area relative to their weight than larger calves. This allows much more heat to be lost rapidly. The calf environment also affects the LCT. A clean, dry hair coat provides greater insulation from cold than a wet, matted coat, and drafts must be avoided because they encourage heat loss. Radiant heat from sunlight and

heat produced during rumination can increase body temperature. Hot temperatures during summer may produce heat stress—calves use additional energy attempting to cool off. Wind or a wet hair coat may increase evaporation and cool the calf. However, humid conditions limit evaporation and contribute to heat stress. Radiant heat from the sun can increase temperature and worsen heat stress.

Most feeding programs are designed to limit the amount of milk or milk replacer fed to calves. In addition, young dairy calves have very little stored fat they can use for warmth. As a result, cold weather can place extra demands on the calf. The amount of feed offered must be increased to provide extra energy. If calves are fed less energy than they need to meet their increased maintenance needs, they will lose weight. The stress of using body tissue to maintain energy levels causes the immune system to be depressed and less responsive to challenges.

Table 2.10 provides an example of the effect of cold temperatures on calf energy requirements; maintenance energy needs may increase 50 to 130 percent when the temperature drops below freezing. The table shows the amount of dry matter from milk replacer or starter that would be required to provide enough energy to maintain normal body functions—continued growth would require even more feed.

While increased energy can come from milk or grain, remember that calves less than 3 weeks of age often do not eat enough starter to provide much extra energy. For these calves, the best way to provide extra energy is by increasing the amount of milk or milk replacer fed. It is recommended that the volume fed be increased as well as the amount of milk replacer powder. This enables you to maintain the same dry matter concentration. The additional milk can be offered in an extra feeding or added to the regular feedings. Continue to provide plenty of fresh grain, as many calves will increase starter intake to obtain more energy. In addition, fermentation of the extra grain will generate heat that helps to warm the calf. Calves beyond 3 weeks of age typically will increase starter intake voluntarily and do not need extra milk. Notice the amount of starter needed rises as calf body weight increases and the temperature drops; table values are requirements in addition to normal milk or starter intake.

Calves need, and will drink, water even during cold weather. Drinking water stimulates starter intake, which will provide calves with more energy and protein than a liquid diet alone. In cold weather, provide warm water three times per day for a mini-

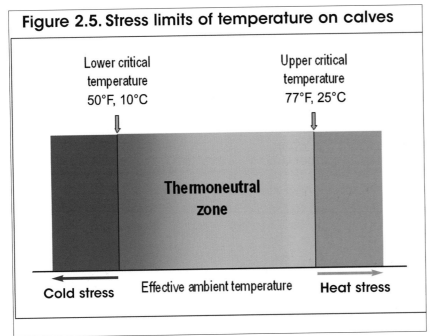

Figure 2.5. Stress limits of temperature on calves

Lower critical
temperature
50°F, 10°C

Upper critical
temperature
77°F, 25°C

Thermoneutral
zone

← Cold stress   Effective ambient temperature   Heat stress →

FIGURE 2.5. The upper and lower critical temperatures listed are general guidelines for month-old calves. Many factors affect the true critical temperatures of an individual calf.

mum of 30 minutes each time to ensure calves have ample opportunity to drink. Hot weather means calves need more water, too. Under short-term heat stress, a calf's need for water is the only nutrient requirement that increases. Water is used to cool the body, and calves must drink more water to replace that lost by panting and increased respiration.

SUCCESSFUL WEANING STRATEGIES

Many producers regularly and successfully wean calves at 4 to 6 weeks of age. Weaning at this age is cost effective because it gets calves started on dry feeds sooner, saving money on labor and feed costs. While weaning calves early makes good sense economically, it is essential that adequate rumen development occurs before weaning. Without a fully functional rumen, calves will be unable to utilize nutrients provided in the post-weaning dry feed diet. The result is a growth slump for 1 to 3 weeks after weaning. Keep in mind, this growth slump after weaning can occur at any age if the rumen is not well developed. As discussed previously, consumption of calf starter and water

Table 2.10. Increased feed requirements for calves due to cold temperatures[1]

	Temperature (°F/°C)										
	>59 / 15	50 / 10	41 / 5	32 / 0	23 / -5	14 / -10	5 / -15	-4 / -20	-13 / -25	-22 / -30	<-22 / <-30
Increase in NEm[2] (%)											
All calves	0	13	27	40	54	68	86	94	108	121	134
Increase in NEm (Mcal/d)											
80-lb (36 kg) calf	0.00	0.17	0.34	0.51	0.69	0.86	1.09	1.20	1.37	1.54	1.70
100-lb (45 kg) calf	0.00	0.20	0.41	0.60	0.81	1.02	1.29	1.41	1.62	1.82	2.01
120-lb (55 kg) calf	0.00	0.22	0.47	0.69	0.93	1.17	1.48	1.62	1.86	2.09	2.31
140-lb (64 kg) calf	0.00	0.25	0.52	0.77	1.04	1.32	1.66	1.82	2.09	2.34	2.59
Starter DMI[3,4] (lb/d, g/d)											
80-lb (36 kg) calf	0.0	0.1	0.3	0.5	0.6	0.8	1.0	1.1	1.2	1.4	1.5
		45	136	227	272	363	454	499	545	636	681
100-lb (45 kg) calf	0.0	0.2	0.4	0.5	0.7	0.9	1.2	1.3	1.4	1.6	1.8
		91	182	227	318	409	545	590	636	726	817
120-lb (55 kg) calf	0.0	0.2	0.4	0.6	0.8	1.0	1.3	1.4	1.7	1.9	2.1
		91	182	272	363	454	590	639	772	863	953
140-lb (64 kg) calf	0.0	0.2	0.5	0.7	0.9	1.2	1.5	1.6	1.9	2.1	2.3
		91	227	318	409	545	681	726	863	953	1 kg
Milk replacer DMI[3,5] (lb/d, g/d)											
80-lb (36 kg) calf	0.0	0.1	0.2	0.3	0.4	0.5	0.6	0.6	0.7	0.8	0.9
		45	91	136	182	227	272	272	318	363	409
100-lb (45kg) calf	0.0	0.1	0.2	0.3	0.4	0.6	0.7	0.8	0.9	1.0	1.1
		45	91	136	182	272	318	363	409	454	499
120-lb (55 kg) calf	0.0	0.1	0.3	0.4	0.5	0.6	0.8	0.9	1.0	1.1	1.2
		45	136	182	227	272	363	409	454	499	545
140-lb (64 kg) calf	0.0	0.1	0.3	0.4	0.6	0.7	0.9	1.0	1.1	1.3	1.4
		45	136	182	272	318	409	454	499	590	636

Adapted from Nutrient Requirements of Dairy Cattle, 2001.
1 - Lower critical temperature assumed to be 59 °F (15°C)
2 - Increase as a percentage of the requirement at thermoneutral conditions
3 - Intake of either starter or milk replacer that will provide enough additional energy to meet increased NEm requirement
4 - Starter containing 1.12 Mcal/lb of NEm, 18% protein
5 - Milk replacer containing 1.86 Mcal/lb NEm (20% protein, 20% fat)

lead to production of VFA that stimulate rumen development. Early starter and water intake are key to early weaning.

With proper care and management, the vast majority of calves can be weaned by 5 weeks of age; however, weaning decisions should not be based on the calendar alone. Most important is the amount of starter eaten by the calf. You should provide individual adjustments to weaning that keep unhealthy calves on milk and allow healthy calves to switch to dry feed. If five-week weaning fails, look for and remove other limiting factors, such as not feeding adequate colostrum, poor ventilation, not feeding high quality calf starter, wet/damp housing, or other stresses on calves. At weaning, calves face significant stress due to changes in their diets, housing and environments. As a result, calves may lose weight, eat less and become more susceptible to infection. The key to limiting this post-weaning slump is to minimize stress around weaning time.

Do not wean calves less than 4 weeks of age, and be sure calves eat 2 pounds (0.9 kg) of grain for 3 consecutive days before weaning. Adequate grain intake ensures continued adequate energy intake after weaning. Obviously, to know the calf is eating 2 pounds (0.9 kg), you must know how much starter

Milk may be stopped abruptly when weaning, but make changes in dry feed gradually. Weaning is stressful for the calf, and to avoid a slump in performance, try to minimize this stress. Do not immediately move the calf to group housing at the same time you wean her.

is fed each day. Weigh out 2 pounds (0.9 kg) of starter and mark the amount on the container used to feed calves to ensure accuracy. Although milk may be removed abruptly, it is recommended that changes in dry feed be made gradually. Feed the same starter for a week and then mix starter with the weaned-calf grain to allow calves to adjust gradually to their grower diet.

Give calves time to adjust to weaning before adding the stress of moving and adapting to group housing. Wait a week after weaning before you move calves to new housing, and limit groups of newly weaned calves to four to six animals to ease the transition. This allows calves to adapt to the social aspects of group housing. Small groups ease the stress of competition for shared feeding and resting areas. The first group post-weaning appears to be the most important for social adaptation. Beyond this first small group, subsequent groups can be much larger and quite different in terms of feeding systems and management with little, if any, detrimental effects on the health and growth of the young heifer.

Since calves commonly encounter a wider variety of pathogens when moved to group housing, only healthy calves should be weaned. Not only will weaned calves be exposed to more pathogens; their immune systems also might be suppressed by the stress of changing diets. Housing areas must have adequate ventilation to reduce the risk of respiratory infections. In addition, major changes in housing temperature can create stress. The area should be clean and well bedded to limit exposure to fecal pathogens. Continue to feed a coccidiostat in the ration to reduce the risk of coc-

Calf feeding guidelines from birth to weaning

Day 1 _Feed 2 to 3 quarts (2 to 3 L) of colostrum in the first feeding as soon after birth as possible (within 1 hour) and again 8 hours later._

Day 2 _Continue to feed colostrum, if available; otherwise feed transition milk or milk replacer. Provide clean water._

Days 3–27 _Feed milk or milk replacer at 10 to 12% of body weight and continue to provide fresh, clean water daily. Introduce small quantities of calf starter on Day 3; keep it fresh and available at all times. Adjust milk feeding to calf weight, calf health, and weather conditions._

Days 28–35 _Healthy calves should be eating 1.5 to 2 pounds (0.7 - 0.9 kg) of calf starter per day by this time. Continue to provide clean, fresh water daily. To encourage starter intake before weaning, milk feeding can be reduced by 25 to 50%._

Days 28–56 _Wean healthy calves once they are eating 2 pounds (1 kg) of grain for 3 consecutive days. Continue to provide clean, fresh water daily. Remember that water needs will increase when milk feeding stops._

cidiosis; weaned calves are especially susceptible to this disease because the stress of weaning can depress the immune system.

Avoid dehorning or vaccinating calves around the time of weaning as well. These are additional stresses to the calves' systems, and they are relatively easy to plan around. Finally, weaning during weather extremes can increase stress. Weather can stress calves by changing energy requirements and suppressing the immune system. Adding the stress of weaning may be too much and might encourage infection and/or weight loss.

HANDLING & HOUSING

You can improve animal handling by better understanding their behavior. Cattle perceive sights and sounds much differently than humans. Cattle are prey animals, and when faced with a dangerous situation, they automatically respond with protective behaviors. Some behavior patterns are rigid, while others can be modified by experience or learning. Repetitive rough, loud handling can create chronic stress that reduces the ability to fight disease. Working with young calves provides opportunities to provide positive experiences with human contact, reducing fear and stress associated with handling.

Cattle have long memories. Cattle can develop permanent fear memories of specific people, places and things. Painful or frightening experiences may be remembered for months or even years. The use of nose tongs and cattle prods must be discouraged. These elicit strong fear memories and make future handling extremely difficult. On the other hand, frequent, gentle handling of young calves will reduce stress (for animals and people) during future handling. Cattle can be trained to adapt to handling procedures over time, even if the procedures are stressful initially. Repeated gentle handling will allow calves to adapt to procedures such as use of headlocks, use of a halter or regular weighing. Training also can be used to reduce stress from unexpected events; for example, providing constant background sound from a radio may allow calves to adapt to noise and

reduce stress from unexpected noises.

Walking animals through new restraint facilities without actually treating them will reduce stress and improve their willingness to enter restraint the next time. An example of this principle is allowing calves to adjust to using headlocks before using headlocks as a restraint device. Calves held in headlocks for the first time and dehorned at the same time will likely associate headlocks with pain. These calves will be more difficult to restrain in headlocks in the future (perhaps when vaccinated a few months later), and may even refuse to use headlocks to eat. Letting calves adjust to headlock restraint before dehorning might avoid this problem for many calves. Allow calves to use headlocks for several days before locking them in. Then lock calves up for a gradually increasing amount of time over several days without treating them. Once calves are used to being in a headlock, treatments may be carried out using headlocks for restraint. Remember not to treat an animal

the first time it is in a headlock.

Begin gentle handling procedures at birth. Newborn calves have just experienced extreme physical stress. Calm, gentle contact with them can reduce physical stress and help avoid psychological stress. Use a towel to rub and massage newborns. This does several important things: stimulates the circulatory system, dries the hair to reduce heat loss, and establishes contact between the calf and a person. Continued contact can be achieved during colostrum feeding. Gently pat the calf and talk to it to reduce its instinctual fear of people. Continue to touch calves and handle them gently during the

When working with young calves, provide them a positive experience so they don't associate human contact and handling with fear and stress.

pre-weaning period. Calves housed individually will have smaller flight zones and less fear of people if human contact is maintained during this time. In addition, gentle handling prevents chronic stress that could suppress the immune system. Finally, practice consistency. Calves experience stress when exposed to new situations. Keep day-to-day feeding and bedding routines, milk temperatures, sounds and people as consistent as possible. When changes are necessary, make them gradually over time so calves can adapt. Take advantage of the opportunity to handle young calves gently and frequently to reduce stress and difficulty in handling older cattle.

Loading and unloading young calves requires some special attention. These calves do not exhibit herding behavior and cannot navigate ramps and inclines. Handling calves individually using a cart or sling is recommended. Typically, young calves will lie down during transport, so

Allow calves to use headlocks for several days before locking them in. Don't treat an animal at the same time it first is held in a headlock.

provide enough space for the calf to do this comfortably. Calves moved any distance often benefit from a feeding of electrolytes when they arrive at their destination. Electrolytes help to reduce dehydration, improve feed intake and assist the immune system in dealing with the stress of transport.

If some of these measures seem too time-consuming, remember that when an animal's immune system is activated due to stress, it comes at the expense of growth. And handling calves gently will pay off when you are dealing with that same animal as an adult, in both its handling and in the milking string.

HOUSING INFLUENCES CALF HEALTH

There are many options available for housing young calves. Cost, labor requirements or availability, climate, personal preference, existing facilities and herd size all are considerations. Although a range of facilities can be used, careful management of the system and individual attention to calves are essential. Housing must provide protection from extreme weather, adequate ventilation, isolation, and a dry, comfortable resting space. If these requirements are met, choice of housing will not limit calf health or growth.

Cold housing systems where the temperature inside is very similar to the

temperature outside are now the most common designs in the U.S. Although calves do very well in cold housing, it is important to protect them from extreme conditions. Remember that calves attempt to maintain a constant body temperature regardless of the outside temperature. Feeding practices must support this, as well as good housing design and management. Use the position of the building, location of openings, and shade cloth or panels to maximize solar heating in the winter and minimize it in the summer.

Design housing to provide a protected, draft-free resting area, yet allow fresh air circulation. This may require removable panels on each pen or hutch that can be used during winter and removed for summer. If solid partitions are used for three sides, a length to width ratio of two to one will provide the calf with an area of draft-free space at the back of the pen. Individual calf housing should provide at least 24 to 32 square feet per calf (2.2 to 2.9 square meters) with a 4 by 6 foot (1.2 by 1.8 m) or 4 by 8 foot (1.2 by 2.4 m) bedded area. Keep pens or hutches well bedded with 6 to 10 inches (15 to 25 cm) of bedding to minimize wet hair coats.

VENTILATION

Proper ventilation eliminates noxious gases, removes excess moisture, and reduces the number of airborne particles. Buildup of noxious gas, such as ammonia, can damage the lungs and respiratory tract of calves and people. It also can stress the calf and suppress the immune system, increasing susceptibility to infection. Airborne particles include pathogens, pollens and dust. Pathogens released when infected animals cough or breathe can travel through the air and infect healthy calves, causing respiratory problems and even permanent

47

lung damage. Excessive moisture in the air contributes to respiratory disease because water molecules carry pathogens and particles. Warm air can hold more water than cold air, so ventilation becomes even more important in warm housing systems and during warm weather.

Proper ventilation makes the air inside as fresh as the air outside. Natural ventilation is both cheapest and often most effective. Orient calf housing to utilize prevailing winds and provide as many openings as possible to take advantage of natural air movement. Typically, open-faced buildings should face southeast; hutches may be faced south in winter and east in summer to maximize air movement and solar heating. Mechanical ventilation using fans or heat exchangers may be required in some designs, especially in warm housing. When evaluating ventilation, be sure to check the air about 6 inches (15 cm) above the bedding surface, as this is the air calves are breathing.

Many devices are available to measure concentrations of dangerous gases, humidity, airflow and temperature in animal environments. In addition to continuously monitoring air quality, devices can automate the operation of fans, vents and curtains. A simple system with a thermometer capable of recording the high and low temperature over a 24-hour period (max-min thermometer) and relative humidity would be adequate for most situations. Ammonia concentrations also can be measured, and often no specialized equipment is required. Most people are able to smell even low levels of ammonia: if you can smell ammonia, there is too much in the environment. Even low levels of ammonia irritate the lungs and bronchial passages, increasing susceptibility to infection.

Ventilation means air move-

ment, but it is not exposure to drafts or gusts of wind. Controlling drafts is accomplished by installing draft barriers on individual pens, not by reducing the ventilation rate in the entire building. During cold weather, windbreaks may be necessary to provide a protected area for the calf, but remember to leave some ventilation. Closing every opening during cold weather is a common, and costly, error that often results in more respiratory problems and less growth. Ideally, calves should have a choice between fresh air and a draft-free area.

ISOLATE CALVES TO LIMIT DISEASE

Isolation is necessary to limit the spread of contagious diseases, especially since young calves are highly susceptible to these diseases. The most common routes of infection are ingestion of fecal material and contact with other animals, particularly older animals. Therefore, young calves must be kept separate from other calves and from older, more mature animals. In addition, management and sanitation practices must be designed to limit the risk of spreading disease between calves. In some situations calves can be housed in small groups successfully; however, these calves will need extra observation and attention to keeping the pen environment clean and well ventilated.

Mature animals can spread many infections to calves. Cows have established resistance to pathogens over time, but calves have very little resistance and are at much greater risk of infection from common organisms. Calves under 2 months of age do not have fully functional immune systems and are less able to produce antibodies to fight disease. For these reasons, young calves should not be housed in a barn with cows and should have no contact with older

animals. If it is not possible to house calves separately from cows, be sure to provide a solid partition between the two groups and direct ventilation to flow from calves to cows.

Nose-to-nose contact between calves can quickly spread an infection from one calf to another, and contact between calves must be limited. Caretakers can also transmit diseases from calf to calf or cow to calf. Sick calves should be fed last using separate equipment. Caregivers should wash their hands and boots before and after working with calves, especially sick ones. Traffic patterns for people, animals and feed should avoid travel from adult cattle to young calves. Additionally, feed refused by cows or heifers should not be fed to younger animals. These practices will limit the risk of spreading infections between animals. Finally, control rodent, cat, bird and fly populations to limit their contact with calves, bedding, and feeds.

KEEP CALVES COMFORTABLE

Comfortable calves are healthy calves that use nutrients for growth, not for dealing with stresses in their environment. Keeping calves dry and well-fed will help them stay healthy. The keys to keeping calves dry are adequate bedding (6 to 10 inches or 15 to 25 cm deep) and drainage. Bedding provides insulation and absorbs moisture. Straw and sawdust are common bedding materials. Both are acceptable, although each has advantages and disadvantages. Straw is soft and provides insulation, but it promotes larger fly populations in summer than sawdust bedding. Sawdust, on the other hand, may be easier to handle, but it can hold more moisture and may be a reservoir for bacterial growth. Bedding materials may be combined as well. For example, straw may be used initially to protect the navel and provide an extra soft bed. Sawdust may be used after the first few days to create a bedding pack with improved drainage. Other possible bedding materials include wood shavings, shredded newspaper, and various plant byproducts such as hulls. In warmer climates, sand or fine gravel can be used to bed calf housing. Exceptionally dusty or moldy bedding can cause eye and throat irritation. Each material has unique characteristics that may fit well with different housing, bedding and manure handling systems.

The amount of bedding required depends on the age of calves, amount of feed and water consumed, and weather. Bedding should be checked daily and added when necessary. Try kneeling for at least one minute on the calf's resting area to test this: your knees should be dry. While kneeling in the winter, your knees should become warmer, not colder. Always remove all bedding after every calf and disinfect the area before bedding for the next calf. Allow the pen to remain empty for 1 to 2 weeks between calves to help limit disease. Drainage also protects the calf from wet conditions. Slope exercise areas slightly to encourage drainage away from resting areas. Place hutches on beds of gravel or rock to allow drainage under bedding materials. Sunlight encourages drying and keeps bedding comfortable, so position hutches to take advantage of sunlight for warmth and drying, especially in the winter.

Calves also need easy access to fresh feed and water at all times for maximum comfort. If fecal contamination occurs, the container should be emptied, washed, disinfected, and dried before refilling. Provide containers that discourage spills and waste. If possible, design housing with feed areas placed outside of the resting area to maintain a cleaner, drier place for calves to lie down. Starter and water spilled into the pen can increase wet conditions and provide an ideal environment for insect larvae.

CONSIDER COST AND LABOR EFFICIENCY

The cost of calf housing options will depend on materials, hardware (such as fans or heaters), and use of existing resources. The maximum number of calves you'll be housing in one year is presented in Table 3.1, with a range of calving intervals and calf mortality rates. The values in the table are calculated for 100 cows and can be extrapolated to any herd size by multiplying the table value (as a decimal) by the number of cows. This table value must then be modified to account for other factors, including: length of time each calf will be housed, number of heifers and bulls housed, seasonal changes in the number of cows calving, and provision of space for 20 to 25 percent more calves than expected to allow down time between calves. Also, culling rates can impact expected calf numbers if herd size changes. Better to have extra pens open rather than doubling up calves or not allowing enough rest time between calves.

Economy of labor addresses the efficiency and accessibility of calf housing. Layout of individual hutches or pens, preparation areas, feed storage, water spigots and bedding storage should consider the number of movements and walking distance required for each task and the order in which tasks are performed. Designated areas for loading and unloading calves must be easily accessible. Protection of employees from inclement weather is an important consideration, but it is secondary to designing a healthy home for calves. Ease of observing and restraining calves and ease of cleaning also contribute to labor economy. Housing that is not easy to maintain is less likely to be cleaned or bedded than a more user-friendly system. There is

Having the feed and water pails outside the resting area helps keep a cleaner, drier bed for the calf.

49

often a direct relationship between labor efficiency and the initial cost of a building. Carefully consider these when planning for new facilities.

OPTIONS FOR CALF HOUSING

Individual calf hutches are very popular and provide excellent shelter because they allow the calf freedom to choose her environment. Hutches allow plenty of natural ventilation (especially when equipped with removable back panels for summer), isolate calves, provide comfortable resting and exercise areas, and have inexpensive construction or purchase costs. Hutches also are easily cleaned between calves. They can be flipped to allow sunlight to thoroughly dry the area, and they can be moved to prevent buildup of pathogens in one location. Hutches do require more labor than other systems, but their benefits in improved calf health and growth often outweigh the greater labor costs. Feed and water may be provided inside or outside the hutch; however, locating them outside tends to improve labor efficiency and keep the resting area cleaner.

The exterior walls of most hutches are made of wood or plastic. Both materials can be effective, although there are pros and cons for each material. For instance, plastic hutches are much easier to disinfect than wooden ones. On the other hand, plywood hutches have lower inside air temperatures than polyethylene plastic hutches in the summer. Providing shade over polyethylene hutches does reduce the inside air temperature compared to no shade, but even shaded plastic hutches are not as cool as wooden hutches. Opaque plastic hutches reduce sunlight penetration and heat stress in the summer compared to translucent plastic.

Other cold housing systems can provide an excellent environment for calves and improve labor efficiency compared to individual hutches. Many calf housing systems incorporate individual pens in a cold barn. Pen dividers that are solid will limit contact between calves and offer draft protection. Wire panels also may be used for pen dividers, but pens need to be separated to prevent nose-to-nose contact between calves. Although ventilation is improved with wire panels, there is no draft protection. Extra bedding must be provided in cold weather and the ability to add solid sides may be helpful for young or sick calves. Depending on the facility, continual adjustments may be needed to keep ventilation adequate as weather changes occur. Greenhouse-type barns with transparent or translucent coverings will require more frequent adjustment than buildings with wooden or opaque roofs.

The kennel-type building is another cold housing option. In this design several individual pens are built in a three-sided shelter. The building can be portable or permanent, and can be moved or tilted back to allow access for cleaning with a skid-steer. Each pen is 3 to 4 feet (0.9 to 1.2 m) wide and 7 to 8 feet (2.1 to 2.4 m) deep. Plywood hovers can be added for draft protection in the winter and removable panels or curtains in the back allow improved air flow during warmer weather.

In contrast to cold housing systems, warm housing uses mechanical ventilation and heating to control the inside temperature and moisture within a specific range. Warm housing facilities are seldom recommended for new calf facilities because maintaining adequate ventilation is very difficult and costs for construction and operation are much higher than other options. Mechanical ventilation systems may be designed based on room volume or animal numbers (Table 3.2). For the best results, ventilation requirements

Here is a kennel-type shelter for several individual pens. A removal panel in the back allows for greater air flow during warmer weather. Pen sides should not allow nose-to-nose contact between calves.

should be calculated by both methods and the one that produces the greatest air exchange selected. The ventilation system must provide the minimum rate of air exchange at all times and utilize additional fans to increase ventilation up to the maximum required during hot summer weather. Additional ventilation provided by separate fans is preferable to a single high-capacity fan. A single fan cannot maintain constant temperature or humidity. Instead the temperature and moisture levels fluctuate dramatically between warm and cold, damp and dry. The second fan, for mild weather, should operate when the inside temperature exceeds 65°F (18°C), and the third fan, for hot weather, should operate when the inside temperature is more than 70°F (21°C). In cooler weather, warm calf facilities need to be heated to maintain an inside temperature of 60 to 70°F (16 to 21°C).

Heaters typically need to provide 1000 btu/h per calf to keep temperatures in this range. In addition, add insulation with an R value of 20 to the walls and an R value of 33 for the ceiling. A 4 to 6 mil vapor barrier is also required on the side of insulation facing the inside of the building. This plastic barrier prevents water vapor from condensing and soaking into the insulation.

Remember, many systems can work for calf housing. Those that work best incorporate ventilation, isolation, comfort and economy in the design. Detailed versions of several plans for calf and heifer housing are available from the Hoard's Dairyman Plan Service, as well as at the online Bookstore at www.hoards.com

Table 3.1. Expected number of calves born in one year for a herd with constant herd size of 100 cows.

Calf losses	Calving interval (months)				
%	12	12.5	13	13.5	14
0	100	96	92	89	86
1	99	95	91	88	85
2	98	94	90	87	84
5	95	91	88	84	81
10	90	86	83	80	77
15	85	82	78	76	73
20	80	77	74	71	69

On average 50% of calves will be male and 50% will be female.

Table 3.2. Minimum ventilation rates for mechanically ventilated, warm housing for pre-weaned calves.

Weather condition	Room volume method (air exchanges per hour)	Animal number method (cubic feet per minute per calf)
Summer	60	100
Warm	30	65
Mild	12	30
Cold	6	15

Adapted from C. A. Gooch, 2005. Pages 116-127 in Proceedings of Dairy Calves and Heifers: Integrating Biology and Management, NRAES.

With both dehorning and removing extra teats, don't procrastinate: proper timing of these procedures when calves are young greatly reduces stress.

DEHORNING

Dehorning calves is recommended to protect both people and animals. Dehorned animals also can stand closer together and require less space for eating and drinking. Calves should be dehorned soon after the horn button can be felt (2 to 6 weeks of age). At this stage, very little horn tissue is present, and the horns are not fully attached. By 10 weeks of age, horns are securely attached to the skull by a bony anchor and have developed blood and nerve supplies. Dehorning before 2 months of age minimizes pain, stress and risk of infection, and younger calves are easier to restrain. Dehorning should not occur at the same time as weaning; this imposes unnecessary stress on the calf.

Electric or butane irons, caustic paste, and gouge methods can be used in dehorning calves. Dehorning irons are the fastest, easiest and safest of these choices. The heavy-duty dehorning surface holds heat for long periods and kills horn tissue quickly to minimize pain for the calf. The hot surface also cauterizes the wound, minimizing blood loss and the risk of infection. Some research suggests that caustic paste methods cause calves less pain than dehorning with a hot iron. In recent years, methods for reducing the pain of dehorning have been developed. When using a hot iron or gouge method, the combination of a sedative and local anesthetic keep the calves calmer during dehorning. Pain control for the caustic paste method can be provided with a sedative only, although an anti-inflammatory drug may help to reduce the effects of delayed pain. In addition to the benefit of reducing pain for calves, these methods can allow one person to more easily dehorn calves. Work with your veterinarian to develop pain control strategies for your farm. These become increasingly important if calves are more than one month of age before horns are removed. If flies are present at the time of dehorning, apply fly repellent to prevent infection. Continue fly control until the scab falls off and the area heals completely.

To use the hot iron method, first heat the iron and restrain the calf. If horn buttons are not easily located, trim the hair around them with scissors to increase visibility. The dehorning iron should be heated fully (red-hot) before it touches the calf's head. Test the temperature by touching the iron to a piece of wood. If it is hot enough, the iron will leave a black burn mark within seconds. Once the iron is ready, place it over the horn button. Rotate the iron in place for 10 to 20 seconds. A copper-colored ring will appear around the horn button when dehorned properly. If the ring is not continuous, apply the iron again. Repeat this procedure for the other horn. Allow the iron to reheat to red-hot before using it again. Since the dehorning iron does reach high temperatures, it is wise to keep a bucket of water on hand and avoid setting the iron near any flammable materials, including hay, straw and sawdust.

When dehorning calves using a caustic stick or paste, be sure to wear gloves and avoid getting the product on your skin. Clip the hair around each horn button and scrape the button until it is raw. Apply a ring of petroleum jelly around each horn button to prevent paste from running into the calf's eyes. Follow the manufacturer's instructions for applying the product. Don't burn the horn too deeply, stop application when blood oozes slightly and the button looks black. Caustic preparations usually work best on calves up to 6 weeks of age.

Gouge methods of dehorning use a scoop or tube. The tube should fit over the horn button and include about one-eighth of an inch of hair. Push down and twist until the skin is cut; then use the cutting edge to cut under the horn and remove it. Apply antiseptic to the wound. To help minimize infections, thoroughly disinfect the dehorner between calves. In general, gouge methods are the least recommended because they cause more pain, increase the risk of infection, and can contribute to the spread of bovine leukosis.

An alternative to dehorning is selection of polled cattle, which can be accomplished relatively quickly because the polled gene is dominant. It's difficult to estimate savings by putting a cost on dehorning, as the cost that the process "sets back" the animal can be quite varied. One producer estimates $10 to $20 per animal, including equipment, labor and loss of growth and efficiency. Another factor that can't be valued is getting rid of what always is an unpleasant task. The polled gene is more common in Red and Whites, Jerseys, Ayrshires and Milking Shorthorns.

REMOVING EXTRA TEATS

Removal of extra teats is an optional procedure that improves the appearance of the udder and may enhance the health of the mature cow. Extra teats may interfere with teat cup placement, develop into functional glands, or become infected with mastitis. If extra teats are removed, the procedure should be done at a young age, preferably between 1 and 2 months, but not at weaning time. Calves should be restrained and gently laid on the floor in a well-lit area for examination. The four regular teats are usually arranged symmetrically with rear teats placed closer together than front teats (a trapezoid appearance). Extra teats are typically smaller

and may be found beside, between, or behind regular teats. If in doubt about whether a teat is extra, do not remove it. Wait until extras can be determined clearly or leave them alone. If a regular teat is cut, that quarter will never function. Teats can be removed with sharp scissors. Wash and disinfect the area and disinfect scissors before starting. When cutting, hold scissors with the blades pointed toward the tail. Slightly stretch the extra teat and cleanly snip it at its base. Little or no blood should appear. Swab the cut with tincture of iodine and apply fly repellent. Be sure to provide clean, dry bedding to prevent infection. Check the cuts after a couple of days to be sure a scab has formed and reapply fly repellent.

PREVENT CROSS-SUCKING

Calves that suck on the udder of other calves can spread mastitis pathogens and infect the develop-

ing udder. The best way to avoid cross-sucking is to house milk-fed calves so they cannot touch each other. When housed in groups milk-fed calves must be managed more carefully to prevent cross-sucking. Most cross-sucking occurs in the 10 to 15 minutes following milk or milk replacer feeding. Allowing adequate sucking time or providing a dry teat for sucking can reduce cross-sucking behavior. Sucking time can be increased by using nipples rather than open buckets, feeding more milk, reducing the flow rate of milk to extend the meal, or leaving nipple buckets or bottles in place for a few minutes after feeding.

Cross-sucking at weaning is probably motivated by hunger, and gradual weaning may increase cross-sucking if calves housed in groups are hungry. Ensuring that grain intake is adequate (2 pounds, or 1 kg per day for 3 days) before weaning can ease the transition at weaning and reduce cross-sucking. Finally, there are several products available that fit on a calf's nose and cause discomfort to the calf being sucked. These products can discourage cross-suckling when the suckled calf kicks the sucking calf.

MONITORING CALF HEALTH

Calves can go from healthy to gravely ill in less than a single day. Developing a standard operating procedure (SOP) for identifying and treating sick calves is essential so that all employees quickly identify and properly treat sick calves. Each calf should be closely evaluated at least twice a day. Assigning a health score to each calf at one of these daily checks can be a useful way of identifying calves that need further attention. A record of scores over time also can be used to evaluate the calf program. One method for monitoring calf health is a three-part scoring system that considers fecal material, respirato-

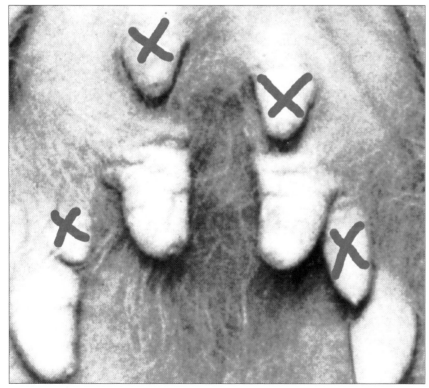

Here the four extra teats are marked with an "X"; note that the regular rear teats are placed closer together than the front teats. Wash and disinfect both the teat area and the scissors, and apply disinfectant to the cuts and then a fly repellant.

ry conditions and general appearance.

In this system, the **FECAL SCORE** considers consistency, color, and odor:

• Score 1 = normal feces of firm to soft consistency that holds its shape; brown to light brown color, and normal odor

• Score 2 = soft to loose consistency similar to pudding that forms a soft pile; yellow, brown, or green color, and a slight odor; mucus also may be present

• Score 3 = loose to watery consistency similar to pancake batter that splatters; yellow or green color, and a strong odor; mucus also may be present

• Score 4 = watery consistency with flakes; yellow or green color, and a strong odor; mucus or slight blood also may be present

• Score 5 = watery consistency and clear color; mucus or blood is present

The **RESPIRATORY SCORE** considers the condition of breathing, nasal discharges, and coughing:

• Score 1 = normal respiration with slow, even breathing and no cough

• Score 2 = slight cough, runny nose, watery eyes; slow, normal breathing

• Score 3 = moderate cough, runny nose, watery eyes; rapid breathing

• Score 4 = moderately severe, very frequent cough; mucus discharge from nose; watery eyes; rapid panting

• Score 5 = severe, chronic cough; irregular, weak breathing to rapid panting; eyes rolling; mucus discharge from nose

The **GENERAL APPEARANCE SCORE**, which often provides the best estimate of the overall well-being of each calf, considers appetite, attitude, and alertness:

• Score 1 = normal appearance: alert, bright eyes, ears up, eager to eat

• Score 2 = slightly off: droopy ears, drinks slowly or plays with milk

• Score 3 = moderately depressed: head and ears droop or head tilted, eyes dull or sunken, lethargic, drinks slowly or does not finish milk

• Score 4 = moderately severe depression: head and ears droop, eyes dull or sunken, will not rise, refuses to eat, weak suckle response

• Score 5 = severe depression: flat on side, will not rise or suckle

---

Figure 4.1. Sample of calf health scoring chart.

ID	Birth date	Week 1	Week 2-3	Week 4-5	Week 6+
1	1/1		RmiP1-1/17	RmiP2 -1/30	
2	1/7				
3	1/10 D P1 1/14				
4	1/12			R/Dmi P1 2/8	
5	1/13				
6	1/20				

D = diarrhea; R = respiratory; p1, p2, p3 = Protocol 1, 2 or 3; mi = mild; mo = moderate; se = severe; following date indicates date of treatment

Here we see that Calf 1 developed mild respiratory problems at 16 days of age, and after Protocol 1 treatment at that time, required Protocol 2 treatment 2 weeks later. Over time, patterns of disease outbreak, successful treatment, chronic problems and so on, give valuable information for managing calf health.

Based on scoring chart developed by Dr. Sheila McGuirk, University of Wisconsin

If any calf receives a score of 3 or more in any of the three areas, measure her temperature, respiration rate and heart rate. When taking a temperature, remember to touch the end of the thermometer to the side of the rectum to measure body temperature not the temperature of fecal material. The normal body temperature range for young calves is 101 to 103°F (38.3 to 39.4°C), with an average of 102°F (38.9°C). Temperatures above 103°F (38.3°C) are considered abnormally high, and a fever-reducer may be considered. Temperatures less than 100°F (37.8°C) indicate the beginning of hypothermia; such calves often benefit from a calf blanket or heat lamp.

Respiration rate can be observed by watching the rise and fall of the ribs. The normal respiration rate of young dairy calves is about 30 breaths per minute, with a range of 24 to 36. Also note the rhythm and depth of the calf's breathing. Normally, the calf will inhale and exhale evenly, or perhaps slightly longer inhalation and breathing is barely noticeable. In a sick animal, breathing is more visible and uneven. In calves, the tail (near its base, on the underside) or jaw provides easy access to arteries for measuring heart rate. In calves less than one month of age, the normal heart rate is about 120 beats per minute with a range of 100 to 140. It is also possible to listen to the heartbeat using a stethoscope (place the stethoscope on the rib cage just behind the point of the elbow). A healthy calf will have a strong, steady pulse; an irregular or weak pulse indicates illness. Remember that after about one month of age, the normal respiration rate, heart rate, and body temperature become more similar to that of mature cattle (body temperature of 100 to 102°F, or 37.8 to 38.9°C, respiration rate of 15 to 30 breaths/minute, and heart rate of 60 to 80 beats/minute).

If any calf receives a fecal score of 3 or more, feed her electrolytes. Check the skin tenting test (described in the section on dehydration) and her general appearance to determine the extent of dehydration and the amount of fluids needed. If her respiratory score or general appearance score is 3 or more, consider giving her an antibiotic. Work with your veterinarian to identify specific treatments and dosages that are the most appropriate for your situation. Other methods of scoring calf health also may work for you; the important part is finding a system that fits your operation.

CONTROLLING DISEASE REQUIRES A COMPREHENSIVE APPROACH

To effectively control disease, all aspects of the infectious disease triad must be addressed. The triad is comprised of host, agent, and environment (Figure 4.2). The interaction of these factors determines whether or not an animal is infected and how sick it gets. Host factors involve the ability of the animal to resist infection. Agent factors address the ability of the infectious agent to cause disease. Environmental factors put the agent in contact with the host. Effectively controlling disease requires action at all three points: increase the animal's ability to fight disease; reduce the number of infectious agents; and minimize contact between host and agent. Host factors like immune status, nutritional status, and stress affect susceptibility to disease. It takes much lower pathogen exposure to cause severe illness in a calf fed

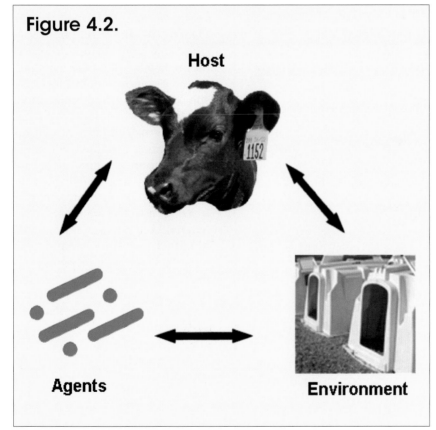

Figure 4.2.

Host

Agents

Environment

FIGURE 4.2. Controlling disease requires a comprehensive approach that considers the entire infectious disease triad, including host, agents, and environmental factors.

very little colostrum than in a calf fed adequate, high quality colostrum. Environmental factors to consider include sanitation practices, housing, ventilation, and isolation. Even a colostrum-fed, well-vaccinated calf is likely to suffer when kept in a dirty, wet, poorly ventilated pen. On the other hand, in an ideal environment with low pathogen loads even calves fed too little colostrum can do quite well.

Generally speaking, keeping the number of infectious organisms low and limiting animal contact with disease agents is more effective than vaccination. However, routine vaccination is useful to prevent the occurrence of common diseases. In this case, vaccination is more cost effective than treating sick animals. Remember that vaccines are just one part of an effective herd health program. In addition, it is impor-

tant to recognize that giving a vaccine (vaccination) does not guarantee the animal will generate a protective level of antibodies (immunization). Animal and management factors influence the effectiveness of vaccination. Stressed or unhealthy cattle do not respond well to vaccination. Plan vaccination schedules to avoid known stressors like weaning or calving, and do not vaccinate sick animals. Calves that receive passive immunity from colostrum may not respond to vaccination in some cases. Maternal antibodies can interfere with active immunity for 6 to 8 months. In addition, calves under 3 months of age may not attain or maintain adequate immunity when vaccinated because their immune systems are not fully developed. Strain differences between vaccines and infectious agents also can cause vaccination to fail.

The handling and storage of vaccines can greatly affect their viability. Be sure to buy fresh vaccines and store them as directed on the label. Follow the manufacturers' recommendations for dose, site and route of administration, and booster schedules. Use a separate, new or sterilized needle for each animal. Modified live virus (MLV) vaccines require extra care because they contain living organisms. Exposure to heat, sunlight, freezing, disinfectants or soap can inactivate these products. Modified live virus vaccines also must be used before their expiration date. Do not mix vaccines unless directed to do so in the manufacturers' instructions. In addition, MLV vaccines lose their effectiveness about 1 hour after being reconstituted. Mix only the amount you will use in 1 hour, and discard any leftover vaccine. Be sure to follow proper disposal procedures for needles and empty containers. Used needles should be put into a hard plastic contain-

---

Table 4.1. Vaccines to consider when developing a vaccination program[1].

Age	Vaccine
Newborn calves	Oral rota-corona
Calves 1 to 2 weeks	Nasal IBR-PI3
Calves 4 to 8 months	Brucellosis (optional)
Calves 6 months	MLV IBR-BVD-PI3-BRSV[2] Clostridium combination Leptospirosis[3]
Heifers 12 to 14 months	Vibriosis if natural service used MLV IBR-BVD-PI3-BRSV[2] Clostridium combination
Bred heifers & dry cows, 6 & 3 weeks before calving	Rota-corona & *E. coli*
Annual booster[4]	MLV IBR-BVD-PI3-BRSV
Booster every 6 months	Leptospirosis

1 - Remember, not all vaccines will be needed in every herd, and this table provides a starting point for discussion with your veterinarian. A one-size-fits-all schedule is impossible, so work with your veterinarian to tailor your vaccination program to address the disease risks specific to your herd.
2 - BRSV requires booster in 2 to 3 weeks. Although modified live virus (MLV) vaccines are recommended, killed products may also be effective, if boosters are administered properly.
3 - Lepto booster required in 2 to 3 weeks. Typically a 5-way combination; consider adding *Hardjo bovis* if early embryonic death is suspected.
4 - Use modified live virus (MLV) vaccine for open cows and killed vaccine for pregnant cows. Administer booster shots as directed by the product label.

er with a small opening and a clear label (sharps container). Blood-contaminated materials should be labeled as biohazards. Sharps, vaccine containers and biohazards should be discarded according to your local environmental and safety regulations.

Vaccines and antibiotics have several routes of administration. For calves, common techniques are intramuscular (IM), subcutaneous (SC), oral, and intranasal (IN). The proper route of administration will be listed on the product label. Failure to follow label directions may result in failure of immunization. Improper administration also may increase allergic reactions.

Intramuscular injections allow medicines to be absorbed into the bloodstream quickly and circulate throughout the body. Needles used are 1 to 1.5 inches (2.5 to 3.8 cm) long and 16- or 18-gauge diameter. Needles should be inserted perpendicular to the skin. Avoid intramuscular injections when possible because they cause long-lasting damage to muscle tissue. When the IM route must be used, inject into muscles of the neck rather than the thigh and never inject more than 10 cc at one location. Before making an IM injection, pull back the plunger on the syringe. If blood is drawn up, reposition the needle.

Subcutaneous injections allow slower absorption of vaccines. Needles used should be 1 inch long (2.5 cm) and 16- or 18-gauge. Injections are made at an angle to the skin. Inject SC medicines under the loose skin of the neck. Pinch the skin to create a space for the injection. Some vaccines for newborn calves may be given orally. No needle is required; simply place a plastic syringe between the teeth and cheek and slowly depress the plunger. Tilt the calf's head up slightly while giving the vaccine and release it

when the vaccine has been swallowed. Intranasal vaccines are useful for respiratory diseases because they stimulate the production of IgA antibodies that protect the surface of mucosal membranes. Needles are not used to give these vaccines. Instead, special aerosol applicators are attached to the syringe. Place the applicator in the nose and depress the plunger. The head should be in a normal position; a reaction of sneezing or coughing is not unusual.

Vaccination schedules vary from farm to farm and in different regions because the diseases that are most common vary. The program outlined in Table 4.1 provides general vaccination guidelines. Consult with your veterinarian to develop an appropriate program for your farm. Consider your farm's disease history and risk to prevent wasting money on unnecessary vaccines and to ensure that all needed vaccines are included.

The remainder of this chapter will focus on specific illnesses of young dairy calves with discussion of causes, treatment, and prevention for each disease. Although these recommendations will apply to many situations, we advise each producer to work with their veterinarian to develop specific protocols for their situation.

WHAT IS CALF SCOURS?

Calf scours, or neonatal diarrhea, is the most common cause of sickness and death in young dairy calves (60.5 percent of calf deaths in the U.S. according to a 1996 survey). Scours is actually a symptom, not a disease. It may indicate infection by bacteria, viruses or protozoa. It also can result from nutritional or environmental stress. Environmental stresses include extreme heat or cold, wet or damp conditions, and changes in housing. Dietary causes of calf

scours include malnutrition (caused by feeding poor quality milk replacer or insufficient quantities of milk), abrupt dietary changes, or excess protein and fat in the calf's diet. Daily fluctuation in the nutrient content of feeds is a common cause of nutritional scours.

The contents of the calf's intestine change continually. Fluids are secreted into the intestine from the bloodstream and absorbed back into the bloodstream from the intestine. When this fluid exchange is functioning normally, the calf is healthy and excretes semisolid feces. However, if the fluid exchange is disrupted and absorption is reduced or secretion is increased, the calf produces runny or watery feces, or scours.

DEHYDRATION KILLS CALVES

Scours kills calves because water, electrolytes, sugars and amino acids that calves need are passed out of the body in watery feces. Fluid loss can easily cause a calf to lose 10 percent of its total body weight in just one day. Considering this enormous fluid loss, it should be obvious that dehydration is the most dangerous effect of scouring. Dehydration is a progressive problem, and typical signs vary by degree of water loss (Table 4.2).

Caregivers must be able to recognize the signs of dehydration, the earlier the better. A simple test that can help you determine the extent of dehydration is the skin tenting test. To test skin tenting, firmly pinch the folds of skin around the neck. If the calf is normally hydrated, skin will quickly return to normal when released. A dehydrated calf will exhibit tenting of skin for several seconds after the pinch is released. The longer tenting lasts, the greater the dehydration. If tenting lasts 2 to 6 seconds the calf is moderately dehydrated. Tenting for longer than 6 seconds indicates severe dehydration. In addition to dehydration, scouring calves also may experience increased energy requirements, appetite loss, depression, electrolyte imbalance (leading to nervous activity), acidosis, failure to rise or death. Catching early warning signs of illness improves the odds that calves will survive scours. People familiar with the individual behavior of each calf will be more likely to notice these small changes.

BACTERIA COMMONLY CAUSE CALF SCOURS

Colibacillosis, or *Escherichia coli* infection typically occurs in the first 1 to 5 days of life. There are several forms of *E. coli* infection due to different strains of the bacteria and different routes of infec-

tion. The enterotoxemic form is caused by *E. coli* strains, such as K99 and F41, that attach to the intestinal wall and produce a toxin. Severe electrolyte imbalances result when the calf's system attempts to flush out the toxin. Death sometimes occurs before diarrhea is observed, but typically the calf has profuse, watery diarrhea. Affected calves die from rapid and severe dehydration rather than infection. Other symptoms include below-normal temperature, depression and failure to rise.

Another type of *E. coli* infection is the enteropathogenic (or attaching and effacing) form. In this case bacteria attach to intestinal cells and destroy them. Typically this infection is characterized by severe diarrhea, often with blood or mucus, that causes rapid weak-

ness and dehydration. A fever may be present in early stages, but the temperature soon returns to normal or below normal.

A final form is called septicemic, meaning the infection invades the blood stream and penetrates all tissues of the body. This is a very rapid disease, often with no evidence of diarrhea. Calves become rapidly depressed and weak, and may die within 12 hours of the onset of symptoms. If calves survive the initial infection, swelling and inflammation of the joints commonly occurs as a secondary infection, sometimes crippling calves so much they must be culled. Septicemia arises from infection of the navel at birth or ingestion of bacteria before first colostrum feeding.

If caught in time, oral rehydration therapy is critical for treat-

Table 4.2. Clinical signs of dehydration.	
% Dehydration	**Symptoms**
5 to 6%	Few clinical signs; diarrhea, strong suckling reflex.
6 to 8%	Sunken eyes, skin tents for 2 to 6 seconds, mild depression, dry mouth and nose, suckling reflex still present.
8 to 10%	Depression, loss of body weight, more distinctly sunken eyes, skin tents for > 6 seconds, dry mucous membranes, increased pulse, failure to rise.
10 to 14%	Comatose, cool ears and legs, skin does not flatten after tent test, poor pulse, failure to rise.
Over 14%	Death.

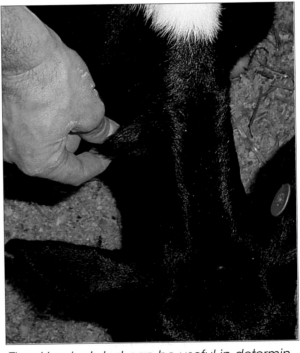

The skin pinch test can be useful in determining the extent of dehydration. To test skin tenting, firmly pinch the skin on the calf's neck and watch to see how long it takes for skin to flatten back into its normal position.

ment of *E. coli* cases. Broad-spectrum antibiotics and anti-inflammatory drugs also can be used. Maintain clean calving areas and calf housing to help prevent *E. coli* infections. Additionally, dip every calf's navel in iodine and feed adequate colostrum. Vaccinations are available for cows (2 to 4 weeks pre-calving) and for calves. The vaccines target strains that use the K99 protein to attach to the intestine.

<u>Salmonella</u> infections may occur at any age, but young calves commonly show symptoms between 14 and 28 days of life. *S. typhimurium* and *S. dublin* are the most prevalent pathogens. Salmonella infections are characterized by severe, watery diarrhea with dehydration and depression. An elevated temperature (103 to 104°F; 39.4 to 40°C) followed by coma is common. Blood and mucus sometimes are observed in feces. Calves go off feed, become weak, and death occurs within 24 to 48 hours of onset due to septicemia. Oral rehydration therapy is possible if the infection is discovered early. Prevention of salmonella infection requires strict sanitation and isolation of sick animals because they contaminate everything they touch. Fecal material from birds, cats, rodents, contaminated water or a human carrier can spread the disease. Salmonella also lives for long periods in the environment, but it is killed by sunlight. *S. typhimurium* can infect humans, so calf care personnel must practice good hygiene and wash their hands after working with sick calves.

<u>Clostridium perfringens</u> types B and C can cause diarrhea in calves within the first 5 to 10 days of life. This organism is a normal inhabitant of the intestine; problems occur when bacteria numbers increase drastically. Clostridial infections often result in sudden death syndrome. The organism

---

Causes of Scours

There are several causes of scours, including increased permeability, hypersecretion, and osmotic imbalance.

Increased permeability of the intestine allows excess fluid from the blood to enter the intestine. The intestine cannot absorb all the excess fluid, and scours result. The permeability of the intestine can be increased by inflammation or injury caused by infection. Cryptosporidia and coccidia parasites cause this type of diarrhea.

Hypersecretion occurs when the intestine is stimulated to produce excess fluid. Intestinal cells are not damaged in this case; they just work overtime. Endotoxins produced by E. coli can stimulate hypersecretion as the calf tries to flush out the toxin.

Osmotic scours occur when the balance of osmotic pressure is upset. Usually, this is caused by a buildup of undigested particles in the intestine. Then, to even out the osmotic pressure, water is drawn into the intestine, which results in diarrhea. Osmotic scours are commonly called nutritional scours because dietary nutrient imbalances or rapid diet changes can upset the balance of osmotic pressure. Dramatic variability in nutrient content of feeds (such as when feeding transition or waste milk) can cause this type of scours due to increased amounts of undigested nutrients in the intestine. In the same way, high rates of liquid feeding may cause softer feces that resemble scours. Osmotic scours may be caused by a failure of absorption or digestion. Failure of absorption is usually caused by physical destruction of intestinal epithelial cells. Rotavirus and coronavirus are pathogens that can cause this destruction. Failure of digestion is usually caused by poor quality feed ingredients, allergens, trypsin inhibitors, or disorders of the intestinal tract. It may also result from feeding large amounts of nutrients at one time. Digestion failure usually leads to poor absorption.

---

kills by producing a systemic toxin that damages tissue. Although affected calves are often found dead without having shown any symptoms, some possible early signs are listlessness, uneasiness, and kicking at the abdomen. Sometimes blood is observed in the feces, and a postmortem exam often finds segments of the intestine are reddened and inflamed. Wet or humid conditions seem to favor overgrowth of this organism. Infections also occur after overeating or consuming poor quality milk replacer. Improper mixing of milk replacer and of oral rehydration solutions also may contribute to clostridial disease if the solutions provide a slug of carbohydrates. Treatment of clostridial infections is often not possible because of rapid death, but if an outbreak occurs, susceptible calves can be given antitoxin and oral antibiotics. Cows can be vaccinated for clostridium before calving, and improper feed mixing or overfeeding should be avoided.

VIRAL INFECTIONS CAN COMPLICATE DISEASE

Rotavirus and coronavirus infections typically occur in the first 5 to 15 days of life. Both rotavirus and coronavirus are shed by most adult cattle and are often picked up by the newborn in the calving pen. Infection by either of these viruses alone usually causes mild diarrhea. However, when the two infections are combined or when a viral infection is combined with a bacterial infection, the infection is more serious. Both rotavirus and coronavirus damage intestinal cells, although coronavirus is more virulent than rotavirus. Damage to the cells of the intestinal lining makes them more susceptible to other invading organisms. Clinical symptoms of these pathogens include watery diarrhea, loss of appetite and depression. Oral rehydration therapy is critical for treatment of these infections. Vaccines are available for cows or calves and usually include a combination of rotavirus, coronavirus and *E. coli*.

Bovine viral diarrhea (BVD) is a rare cause of diarrhea in calves, but it is a common respiratory pathogen and may cause severe suppression of the immune system that allows other pathogens to become rapidly fatal. Antibodies in colostrum usually provide protection for calves through 3 to 6 months of age. Calves affected with BVD reveal ulcerations throughout the digestive tract when examined postmortem. In acute cases, ulcers are found on the tongue, lips and mouth. Persistently infected, or PI, calves acquire BVD from their dam before birth. These calves may appear perfectly healthy or may be poor doers; in either case they can shed millions of BVD viral particles in their secretions and excretions. Vaccinations are available to limit bovine viral diarrhea. Work with your veterinarian for to develop a plan to identify PI animals and schedule appropriate vaccinations.

PROTOZOA ARE ANOTHER SOURCE OF INFECTION

Cryptosporidia infections can occur any time between 5 and 35 days of age, but commonly occur between 14 to 21 days. *Cryptosporidium parvum*, the most commonly isolated organism, is a parasite found in the intestinal tract and feces of mammals. Under normal conditions calves do not become sick due to cryptosporidia, but calves under stress or infected by another organism are more susceptible to infection. *C. parvum* damages cells lining the intestine, which can cause serious diarrhea, emaciation, depression and dehydration. Often calves appear to starve even though their appetite remains near normal.

No specific therapy exists for cryptosporidiosis; keep calves warm, dry, and well fed. Oral rehydration therapy is critical for treatment of this disease if diarrhea is present. If the infection is not complicated by multiple pathogens, calves usually recuperate in 5 to 10 days. Cryptosporidia are found on nearly every farm, and nearly all calves shed these organisms.

To prevent infections, which are spread by fecal contact, feed colostrum at birth and follow strict hygiene: calving areas, calf housing, and equipment used to transport calves should be cleaned and dried (by sunlight if possible) after every calf. Feeding equipment also should be sanitized and, if possible, different equipment used for each calf. Rats and mice are carriers, so keep them out of feed and equipment. *C. parvum* is a human pathogen, and calf care personnel must practice good personal hygiene and wash hands after handling calves, especially scouring calves.

Coccidiosis is another common infection caused by protozoan parasites of the Eimeria species. In cattle the most common infectious organisms are *E. bovis* and *E. zuernii*. These infections can begin around 3 weeks of age and calves are susceptible through 2 years of age. Outbreaks often occur around 4 to 6 months of age due to the waning of passively acquired immunity, greater exposure to coccidia in group housing near older animals and the stresses of transitions in feed. This parasite causes acute and subclinical infections and damages cells lining the intestine.

Calves are more susceptible to infection when stressed and during cool weather. Acute cases show soft feces in the early stages, and symptoms progress into watery, often bloody, diarrhea. Calves have normal temperatures, but lose weight and become anemic. Dehydration and death can occur within 24 hours. Subclinical infections, which are more common, reduce growth rate but produce no other outward signs of illness. Feed additives in milk replacer, water, or starter can be used to kill or reduce the growth of coccidia and prevent losses. Approved feed additives for preventing coccidiosis are decoquinate, lasalocid, and monensin. Amprolium is approved for treating calves that are infected.

For the best control, begin feeding a coccidiostat by about 3 days of age. Coccidia oocysts are shed in manure and older animals that have built up immunity to coccidiosis continue to shed oocysts. These can survive for long periods in the environment, even in extreme weather.

PREVENTION OF CALF SCOURS

Although diarrhea is a common problem and the primary cause of calf illness and death in the US, it can be controlled with proper management of colostrum, environment, nutrition and stress. Colostrum feeding is the most important factor in preventing calf scours. Without colostrum, the calf has no protection against infection. Feeding large amounts of high quality colostrum as soon as possible after birth provides the calf with passive immunity against potential pathogens and is the best preventative measure. The importance of colostrum cannot be overemphasized. If cows are vaccinated before calving, colostrum will contain additional antibodies for common scour-causing organisms.

The environment is the next important aspect in preventing diarrhea. Calving areas need to be clean and dry and should be cleaned after every calving. Immediately after birth, the navel should be dipped in tincture of iodine to begin drying it out and prevent bacteria from entering through it. Calves should be moved to clean housing with plenty of fresh bedding. It is best to clean and disinfect calf housing between each calf and allow 1 to 2 weeks between occupants. Housing should be separate from older animals and should have adequate ventilation without being drafty. Bedding should be maintained so calves always have clean, dry places to lie down. Calves should not have contact with each other or with other animals.

Rodents, cats, birds and flies should be controlled to prevent fecal contamination of feeds and bedding. Fecal material is the most common source of infection. Follow strict cleaning and sanitizing procedures to properly disinfect all feeding utensils and equipment, and consider individual feeding equipment for each calf to minimize spread of organisms. Isolate sick calves and feed them last, using separate feeding equipment. It is also advisable to wear disposable gloves or wash your hands after working with sick calves.

Consistency in the composition, timing, and temperature of liquid feeds also will help prevent scouring. Calves become accustomed to

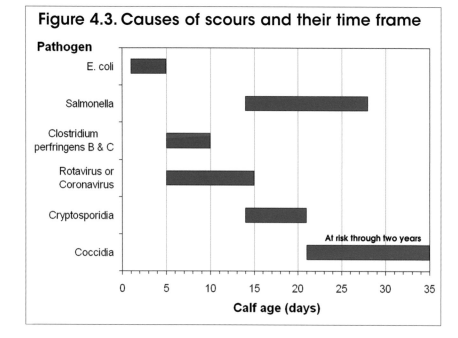

Figure 4.3. Causes of scours and their time frame

Pathogen

- E. coli
- Salmonella
- Clostridium perfringens B & C
- Rotavirus or Coronavirus
- Cryptosporidia
- Coccidia — At risk through two years

Calf age (days)

Absorption and secretion of the intestine

The intestine is a semi-permeable membrane, and water flows across the intestine in response to the concentration of solutes (molecules that are in a solution). When the amount of solutes is high on one side of a semi-permeable membrane, water from the side with a low concentration is drawn across the membrane to dilute the contents on the side with a higher concentration. The number of molecules in a solution can be described by osmotic pressure. A solution with high osmotic pressure will draw water to it to dilute the contents. In the case of the intestine, as the concentration of solutes in the intestine increases, water is drawn out of the body into the intestinal lumen; the reverse is also true. Intestinal cells can also actively affect water movement by pumping ions into or out of the intestinal lumen to change the osmotic pressure.

Sodium plays an important role in establishing osmotic pressure gradients that influence water movement. As a general rule, when sodium moves across the intestine, water follows. The primary route of sodium absorption is via co-transport with glucose or amino acids. This means that sodium absorption, and subsequently water absorption, is more efficient when glucose or amino acids are present in the intestinal lumen.

a routine and will have the least stress if that routine is followed. Avoid feeding poor quality feeds and be sure to feed enough to meet nutrient requirements. The addition of coccidia medications to feeds may also be helpful in preventing scours and minimizing stress on the calf. Feeding coccidiostats and ionophores positively impacts calf and heifer growth up to 24 months of age. Other stresses, such as long distance transportation and overcrowding should be minimized as well. Pay attention to calving ease ratings when selecting sires, and monitor close-up cows to prevent prolonged calving times that result in weak calves at birth.

A summary of these common pathogens and the typical age at which calves are affected by each pathogen appears in Figure 4.3. Regular use of fecal culture and postmortem examinations can help you identify common pathogens on your farm and provide useful information for developing prevention and treatment programs.

FLUID REPLACEMENT THERAPY IS BEST SCOURS TREATMENT

Recall from the discussion of dehydration that fluid loss is the most serious threat to the calf's life; therefore, fluid replacement is the most important treatment. In addition to water, scouring calves lose many important nutrients that are dissolved in the fluid. Oral rehydration or fluid replacement therapy relies on the use of specially formulated products that replace lost fluids, replenish lost nutrients, and restore pH to normal. These products are commonly called electrolytes, and while electrolytes are one kind of ingredient, a true oral rehydration solution contains several other important ingredients. A summary of the recommended amount of each of these ingredients is provided in

Appendix Table 1, page 70.

Water loss as a result of diarrhea usually leads to dehydration. Direct loss of electrolytes in fluids and the accumulation of metabolic wastes due to reduced urine output cause blood pH to drop; the calf develops acidosis. Many oral rehydration solutions contain ingredients that help to raise the pH back to normal levels.

COMPONENTS OF ORAL REHYDRATION SOLUTIONS

Water is the first and most essential part of an oral rehydration solution. It corrects dehydration and serves as a carrier for the other ingredients in the solution. Water is involved in every aspect of metabolism and transports nutrients throughout the body. Among its many functions, water helps to regulate body temperature, digest feeds, eliminate wastes and lubricate joints. Scouring calves will often voluntarily increase water consumption if fresh water is provided. However, it is impossible to restore fluids lost during diarrhea by feeding water alone, especially when viral or bacterial infection has disrupted the normal absorption process in the intestine.

Sodium is an important component of oral rehydration solutions. Its purpose is to increase water absorption and help restore pH to normal. Sodium is the major ion in the fluid surrounding body cells (the extracellular fluid). When sodium is absorbed into an intestinal cell, it is quickly pumped out into the extracellular fluid. This creates a gradient of osmotic pressure that draws water from the intestine into the body. The increase in sodium concentration causes the hydrogen ion concentration in blood to fall, which raises pH. Sodium is tightly regulated by the body and although a drop in the sodium available for metabolic functions (due to diarrhea,

for example) can cause problems, high amounts also can create problems. If too much sodium is offered in a rehydration solution, calves will need to drink more water to dilute the high concentration. Often this extra water is not available in the pen or calves are too weak to drink it. Sodium should be included in the oral rehydration solution at 70 to 145 mmol/L. For the highest absorption efficiency, the ratio of glucose and glycine to sodium present should be 1:1 and should not exceed 2:1.

Glucose is included to increase the absorption of sodium and to provide an energy source. Some products include large quantities of glucose and are advertised as "high energy." However, even high glucose formulations do not provide enough energy to replace the milk or milk replacer fed to calves. In addition, most of these products do not provide an adequate source of protein. Note that glucose and dextrose are the same; both terms can be found on product labels. No more than 200 mmol/L of glucose should be included.

Glycine is a non-essential amino acid that is commonly added to oral rehydration solutions and has been shown to enhance absorption of glucose. Also, because glycine is co-transported with sodium into cells, it improves water absorption. The typical range for glycine in rehydration solutions is 10 to 40 mmol/L. When glycine is included in a product, both glycine and glucose must be considered when determining the ratio to sodium. The total of glucose plus glycine should be 150 to 200 mmol/L. Other potentially useful amino acids are glutamine and glutamate. Some studies found that these amino acids help intestinal cells repair damage inflicted by pathogens; however, more research is needed before their use can be recommended.

Alkalinizing agents are added to increase blood pH and also may provide some energy for the calf. When alkalizing agents partially replace chloride, absorption of water and sodium are improved. The most common alkalinizing agent is sodium bicarbonate; other compounds include sodium citrate, lactate, acetate or propionate. Sodium acetate is the most easily metabolized of these compounds and does not interfere with milk digestion. Bicarbonate and citrate interfere with digestion of milk; therefore, do not mix products containing these ingredients with milk. In addition, feed the electrolyte product about 4 hours after feeding milk. There is some debate about the best alkalinizing source; however, it is clear that products containing an alkalinizing agent are more effective than products without such ingredients. The total alkalinizing ability from all agents should be 50 to 80 mmol/L.

In addition to sodium, oral rehydration solutions also contain other important electrolytes, especially potassium and chloride. Potassium is the key ion inside cells and is needed for proper nerve function and muscle contraction. Chloride is the major negative ion involved in regulating acid-base balance and water movement in the body. It is essential in maintaining blood pH. Although little research has evaluated the amount of potassium and chloride needed to replenish electrolytes in scouring calves, the range of potassium found in most solutions is 10 to 30 mmol/L and chloride is 45 to 100 mmol/L.

Some products include gelling agents such as guar gum, pectin, psyllium, and others. Research can't prove the benefit of these products, though it would appear that gelling agents reduce diarrhea within hours of feeding and may coat inflamed intestinal mucosa. Slowing down the passage rate of the rehydration solution also may allow the intestine to absorb more nutrients. However, this may also reduce the body's ability to flush out toxins. Another potential drawback of gelling ingredients is that fecal material becomes more firm regardless of the status of scours. This may create the false impression that the calf has recovered and no longer requires treatment. More research is needed to determine the true advantages and disadvantages of gelling agents.

Many rehydration solutions also contain direct-fed microbials. These are bacteria that are meant to re-establish the correct ratios of gut microflora. Usually these probiotics consist of bacillus, lactobacillus, and bifidobacterium species, which work against *E. coli* and are beneficial to the intestinal environment. There is no published research at this time evaluating direct-fed microbials in rehydration solutions. Choose an oral rehydration solution based on its ability to provide correct levels of electrolytes and to rehydrate, rather than whether it contains microbials.

It can be a challenge to compare products. Many oral rehydration products are sold (some current examples are compared in Appendix Table 2, page 71.); be sure to select the type intended for scours treatment. This type should contain nutrients similar to Appendix Table 1. Other electrolyte products are intended as supplements for drinking water or milk replacer. These products do not contain adequate electrolytes for treating scouring calves and are not intended for use in young calves. Supplement products are used to provide extra electrolytes to older, usually weaned calves or mature cattle during times of stress from transport or extreme weather. Typically, supplement products are diluted in large volumes of water or call for very small amounts (teaspoons) of powder.

Recipes for home made electrolyte treatments are available, but generally these do not provide the same balance of electrolytes as commercial products. If you are in a bind and need to make your own, remember not to use table sugar for the glucose portion. Table sugar is sucrose, a carbohydrate that cannot be metabolized by calves because they do not have the enzyme to break it down. Adding sucrose may actually increase scouring and worsen dehydration. A sample recipe for homemade electrolyte solution is provided in the sidebar.

FEED ELECTROLYTES IN ADDITION TO NORMAL MILK DIET

Electrolytes are primarily fed to replace lost water. Logically then, the amount to feed depends on how much water has been lost. A 90-pound calf that is 8 percent dehydrated has lost 90 x 0.08 = 7.2

Recipe for Oral Rehydration Solution

1 tsp low sodium salt (4.2 grams)

2 tsp. baking soda (9.2 grams)

1.75 oz. (1 packet) fruit pectin (approx. 25 g)

1 can beef consommé

Add water to make 2 quarts (2 L). Feed at the rate of 1 pint (0.5 L) per 10 lbs. (4.5 kg) of body weight 3 to 4 times a day. Feed milk 2 to 3 hours before or after due to bicarbonate content.

pints (or 3.5 L) of fluid, and will need an extra 3.6 quarts (3.5 L) of liquid, in addition to its normal liquid intake. In other words, if the calf normally gets 4 quarts (4 L) of milk per day, it will need 7.6 quarts (7.5 L) of liquid per day. Moderate dehydration (less than 8 percent) can probably be treated with one additional 2-quart (2 L) feeding per day. More severe dehydration requires more than one additional feeding. After feeding electrolytes, it may appear that the scours are worse than in untreated calves. Actually, treated calves have more water available because they are less dehydrated.

Electrolytes can be fed by nipple bottle or pail if the calf will drink voluntarily. If the calf is too weak or refuses to suck, use an esophageal feeder. Pass the tube down the left side of the calf's mouth to avoid entering the windpipe. Remember to be patient and gentle when tube-feeding calves. Typically, calves dehydrated more

than 8 percent respond best to intravenous administration of fluids, rather than oral therapy. Often these calves have no suckle reflex and refuse to stand. Do not give products designed for oral use intravenously; work with your veterinarian to determine a treatment strategy for severely dehydrated calves.

Traditionally it was recommended that scouring calves be removed from milk and fed only electrolytes. Research has provided evidence that this is not a good strategy. Figure 4.4 shows the change in body weight during the first 3 days of treatment for calves on three different treatments. Calves fed the normal amount of milk in addition to electrolytes gained weight throughout the 7-day treatment period. Calves fed only electrolytes (no milk) or fed electrolytes and less than the normal amount of milk lost weight during the first 3 days of treatment.

Withholding milk during treat-

ment for scours is counterproductive. Without milk, calves lose body weight, become malnourished, and suffer greater suppression of the immune system. Therefore, feed electrolytes in addition to milk or milk replacer. However, do not feed electrolytes immediately before or after milk feeding, because the solution may interfere with the digestion of milk or milk replacer and cause additional diarrhea. Instead, electrolytes should be fed 30 minutes to 1 hour after milk. Calves normally fed in the morning and afternoon could be fed electrolytes at noon and in the evening. Begin feeding electrolytes at the first sign of diarrhea to prevent rapid dehydration.

ANTIBIOTICS MAY NOT HELP SCOURING CALVES

It is important to realize that antibiotics cannot cure viral or protozoal infections. On the other hand, bacteria may respond to antibiotic treatment, provided the antibiotic used is appropriate for the bacteria causing the infection. Therefore, the first step in administering antibiotics to scouring calves should be to identify the responsible pathogen(s). Color and odor of feces cannot positively identify the invading organism(s). Instead, one must use fecal culture to determine the causative organism(s). Unfortunately, the time required to conduct fecal culture may mean the calf recovers or dies before results are known. However, regular use of fecal culture can identify common pathogens and provide a general strategy for treatment within certain groups or facilities on your farm. Fecal culture results also can be useful in shaping vaccination and disinfection protocols.

Typically antibiotics are most useful when bacteria are the causative agents or when bacterial infections are likely to exist sec-

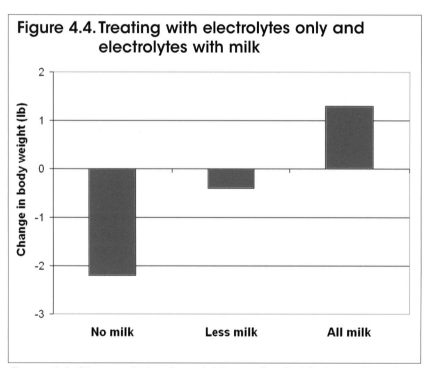

Figure 4.4. *Change in body weight over the first 3 days of treatment in calves treated for diarrhea with electrolytes plus various proportions of their normal milk diet.*
Source: Garthwaite et al, 1994, Journal of Dairy Science 77:835-843. Value for "all milk" estimated from graph.

ondary to viral or protozoal infections. Resistance is another consideration in choosing antibiotic treatment. For instance, most strains of E. coli have resistance to ampicillin, erythromycin, kanamycin, neomycin, penicillin, streptomycin, tetracycline, and sulfonamides. Work with your veterinarian to determine what organism(s) is present and whether or not antibiotics will aid treatment.

Keep in mind that in many cases of diarrhea, more than one organism, environmental factors, nutrition, and management all contribute to the infection. Work closely with your veterinarian to determine causes of scours and to develop a plan to treat sick calves and prevent new infections.

RESPIRATORY DISEASE IS SECOND LEADING ILLNESS

Respiratory disease is any infection of the nasal passages, throat, trachea, bronchial tubes or lungs. Infection of the lungs is more specifically called pneumonia. Respiratory infections are the second leading cause of illness and death in young calves (24.5 percent of total calf deaths in a 1996 survey by USDA). Infections can range from mild to severe and the resulting damage can be temporary or permanent. Calves with chronic pneumonia rarely recover fully and tend to be "poor doers" for the rest of their lives. Such calves will not make profitable replacements and should be culled. Many of the organisms that cause respiratory infections are normally present in the respiratory tract. When the calf is stressed or suffers infection from multiple organisms, normally occurring organisms can cause disease or compound the effects of other pathogens. On the other hand, healthy, nonstressed calves may be unaffected when challenged. Minimizing stress and vaccinating appropriately can largely control

losses from respiratory disease.

Many organisms can cause respiratory infections; some are shown in Table 4.5 on page 68. Infections of the upper respiratory tract (nose, throat, trachea, bronchial tubes) typically result from IBR, BVD, and PI3 organisms. Pneumonia is more often caused by pasteurella species, mycoplasma species, BRSV, and *Histophilus somni* (formerly called *Haemophilus somnus*). Viral infections commonly promote secondary bacterial invasion of the lungs. *Mannheimia hemolytica*, *Pasteurella multocida*, and *Mycoplasma bovis* are the most frequently isolated pathogens in calf pneumonia cases.

These normal inhabitants of the respiratory tract typically do not cause pneumonia on their own. Respiratory disease is often caused by interactions between multiple pathogens. For instance, BRSV or PI3 infection results in damage to the ciliated cells that line the surface of the respiratory tract. Usually these cells sweep bacteria, viruses, dust particles and other foreign material away from the lungs and out of the body in mucus. If they are damaged, however, other organisms can enter the lungs. When the invading bacteria die, they release toxins that destroy lung tissue. As a result, the calf suffers from obstructed airways and reduced lung capacity, which can cause long-term or even permanent tissue damage.

Indications of respiratory disease vary, but often one or more of the following signs is observed: nasal discharge that is initially thin and watery but becomes thick yellow mucus; dry cough; fever (rectal temperature of 103 to 106°F; 39.4 to 41°C); difficult, rapid, or irregular breathing; refusal to eat or slower than normal eating; diarrhea; and a postmortem exam reveals lesions on

the lungs. Early detection of infection helps minimize damage to lungs. Watch calves carefully for any of the signs described above. To properly treat infections, it is necessary to isolate and identify the invading organism(s). Identification must be made within the first 3 to 5 days of the illness to be any help in treating the calf. If bacteria are responsible or likely to cause secondary infections, antibiotic therapy may be useful. Work closely with your veterinarian to develop protocols for treating respiratory disease.

PREVENTING RESPIRATORY DISEASE

There are several key components to preventing respiratory disease in calves. First, consider the factors that predispose calves to infection: not feeding adequate colostrum, high humidity (especially when combined with low temperatures), poor ventilation, drastic temperature changes (more than 25°F between the daily high and low), and stress. Management can control most of these factors. Feed at least 4 quarts of high quality colostrum within the first 8 hours of life. This will give calves passive immunity to many common pathogens found on the farm and protect them for several weeks. Weather is unpredictable and out of management's control, but housing can be designed to minimize the negative impact of bad weather. Provide ventilated, well-drained, draft-free housing with adequate bedding.

All of the other factors boil down to one word: stress. Limit the stresses placed on calves and pneumonia will be much less common and much less severe. Stressful conditions stimulate the production of cortisol, which suppresses the immune system. Increased stress makes the calf less able to fight infections. Furthermore, many stressors cause physical damage to calves that increases susceptibility to disease. Poor ventilation allows irritants like ammonia, methane, hydrogen sulfide, molds and dust to disrupt the surface of sensitive mucous membranes in the respiratory tract. This makes it easier for pathogens to invade the body. Humid air contains water molecules that can transport pathogens, carrying them into the lungs. Proper ventilation can remove most humidity problems.

Nutritional stress, due to underfeeding milk or milk replacer, feeding poor quality feeds, or weaning calves before they are eating enough starter, decreases energy levels and suppresses immune function. Finally, exposure to a large number of pathogens increases the chance that infection will occur. Minimize exposure by housing calves separately from adult animals, older calves, and each other. Keep recently weaned calves in individual housing for a week to allow them to adapt to nutritional changes before facing increased pathogen challenge. Other stresses, such as long distance transportation or grouping of purchased calves from different sources, may be unavoidable. In this case, pay close attention to other management factors and be sure to vaccinate cows and calves.

Vaccinations are recommended to help control organisms that cause respiratory disease, especially viral agents. Your overall vaccination program and schedule should be tailored specifically for your farm to target local pathogens. Annual vaccination of cows and heifers should result in adequate antibody concentration in colostrum. These antibodies will protect calves for several weeks if calves are fed enough colostrum soon after birth. Presence of passively acquired antibodies interferes with vaccina-tion of calves for about 6 months in some cases. The exact timing of the loss of passive immunity depends on the individual calf, the organism, the antibodies present in colostrum, the amount of colostrum fed, and the amount of antibody absorbed by the calf. Therefore, it is recommended that calves vaccinated before 6 months should be revaccinated at 6 months of age to establish active immunity to respiratory disease. Herds experiencing severe problems may consider vaccination beginning at 1 or 2 months and continuing several times until calves reach 6 months. Another option is a nasal vaccine for IBR-PI3 at 1 to 2 weeks of age.

NAVEL INFECTIONS AND HERNIAS

The primary causes of navel infections are a dirty calving environment and delayed dipping of navels. The newborn calf is not able to fight early infections and the umbilical cord provides a direct path to the calf's circulatory system. Navel infections can result in rapid systemic infection and death, but less severe infections lasting 2 to 3 weeks also may occur. Affected calves exhibit a slight fever, listlessness, and swelling around the navel. Provide a clean calving pen, dip the navel of every calf with 7 percent tincture of iodine immediately after birth, and keep calf housing bedded deeply to reduce the chance of these infections. If calves are born into a dirty environment, navel dipping can be repeated 2 to 4 hours after birth and again for 2 to 3 days to completely dry and disinfect the umbilical stump.

The body wall normally closes around the dried umbilical stalk within a few days of birth. Occasionally, umbilical hernias occur due to an inherited condition or infection. Hernias are more common in Holstein calves than other breeds. Openings with a diameter smaller than 0.5 inch (1.3 cm) usually close as the calf grows. Larger openings are more are likely to allow the abomasum, intestine or connective tissue to protrude. Calves typically have no digestive problems; however, the intestines may be blocked by the hernia. Umbilical hernias in calves often are accompanied by an abscess or other infection. Calves with swelling in the navel area should be examined by a veterinarian to determine if surgical correction is needed. Calves also may suffer from internal abscesses due to navel infection. These are often painful and cause arching of the back and poor performance.

RINGWORM

Ringworm is a highly contagious skin disease affecting domestic animals and humans. It is caused by a fungal infection (*Trichophyton verrucosum*) of the hair and skin. Infected calves develop circular lesions covered by a crusty, gray scab. These scabs are most commonly found on the head and neck, but can be found all over the body. Infections are spread directly by contact with infected animals and indirectly by contact with spores in the environment. The infection causes no permanent damage or economic loss and has a high rate of spontaneous cure. However, animals with scabs are prohibited from exhibitions or shows. Also, fungal spores shed by infected heifers can persist in the environment for many years, and the disease spreads easily to humans. Therefore, treatment is often recommended to limit the spread of the infection.

There are a large number of unproven remedies for ringworm, and many appear to be successful only because animals often recover spontaneously. Individual animals are best treated by scrubbing off scab tissue with a stiff brush and soapy water, then applying a topical fungicide. Larger groups of heifers may be treated using a pressure washer and fungicidal solution. Treatment is repeated daily or every other day until lesions begin to dry up and disappear. It is essential to clean housing and feeding areas as well as any handling or grooming equipment used on infected animals. Wear gloves while treating heifers and disinfect brushes or other equipment between animals. Infections may be limited by reducing overcrowding, maintaining proper nutrition including supplementation of vitamins A, D, and E, increasing exposure to sunlight, and providing proper ventilation.

JOHNE'S DISEASE

Although Johne's disease does not directly affect the health of young calves, it is during the first 2 months of life that animals are infected with this debilitating disease. Every effort should be made to prevent the spread of Johne's from cows to calves. The source of most infections is fecal matter, which indicates that the cleanliness of the calving pen is a critical factor in controlling transmission. Immediate removal of newborn calves from the maternity pen also will limit their contact with adult cows and manure. Take care to thoroughly wash the teats and udder of fresh cows before milking to avoid contaminating colostrum with fecal material. Johne's also may be spread directly in milk or colostrum, and herds seeking to eradicate Johne's should consider pasteurization of all colostrum and milk fed to calves or the use of colostrum replacer and milk replacer. If colostrum is not pasteurized, feed milk from test-negative cows and do not pool colostrum. The organism that causes Johne's is very resistant to most disinfectants; choose products that have activity against tuberculin organisms. Vaccinating calves before one month of age is possible; however, the vaccine only decreases the incidence of clinical disease and is not recommended in most situations. Work with your veterinarian to develop a comprehensive plan to limit the spread of Johne's in your herd.

PARASITES

Preweaned dairy calves are frequently affected by *Cryptosporidia* and *Eimeria* species, internal protozoal parasites causing diarrhea and reduced growth. These organisms have been discussed previously. Other internal parasites, such as stomach worms and lungworms and liver flukes, are encountered as calves grow older and go out on pasture. External parasites including flies, grubs, lice, ticks and mites also become problems for older calves and heifers.

Many species of flies are considered dairy pests. Flies transmit disease, including pinkeye and mastitis, and reduce growth rates, so controlling their populations is very important. Blood sucking flies (horn, stable, horse, and deer flies) and mosquitoes, as well as house and face flies, are the most common fly species on dairies. Fresh manure and rotting organic matter are preferred locations for these flies to lay eggs. Housing areas for young calves are often breeding grounds for flies. Since flies have a life cycle of approximately 10 days, weekly removal of all manure, wet bedding, and spilled feed is an effective way to limit fly populations. To limit fly breeding grounds, it is essential to remove wet bedding, not just bury it under fresh straw or sawdust. Chemical treatments and trapping devices also may be useful. Mosquitoes breed in stagnant water, so avoid standing water in or around calf facilities to reduce their populations. Calves may benefit from fly repellents, especially during summer months or after any treatment procedures that leave an open wound. However, the best method of fly control is clean, dry housing with as few potential egg laying sites as possible.

Table 4.3. Common calf pathogens

Organism	Feces	Milk	Saliva/Mucus	In utero	Airborne	Other	Effect on calves
Routes of transmission							
BACTERIA							
Arcanobacterium pyogenes		x	x			flies	respiratory disease, navel infection, heifer mastitis due to cross-sucking
Chlamydia species	x	x	x				respiratory disease, vaginal infection
Clostridium perfringens types B and C	x					soil	diarrhea, tissue damage
Esherichia coli	x	x	x		x	urine	diarrhea, navel infection, septicemia, joint ill
Histophilus somni[1]			x		x	urine	respiratory disease, ear infection
Mannheimia haemolytica[2]		x	x		x		respiratory disease
Moraxella bovis			x			flies	pinkeye
Pasteurella multocida		x	x		x		respiratory disease
Salmonella Dublin	x	x	x	x			respiratory disease, diarrhea
Salmonella typhimurium	x	x	x	x			diarrhea, septicemia
Staphylococcus aureus		x	x				cross-sucking can lead to mastitis
Mycobacterium avium subsp. paratuberculosis (MAP)	x	x		x			Johne's Disease
MYCOPLASMA[3]							
Mycoplasma bovis		x	x		x		respiratory disease, arthritis, infections of ear, eye, and brain, abscesses, heifer mastitis
Mycoplasma dispar		x	x		x		respiratory disease
Ureaplasma species		x	x		x		respiratory disease
PROTOZOA							
Cryptosporidium parvum[4]	x			?		dust	diarrhea
Eimeria bovis	x						diarrhea
Eimeria zuernii	x						diarrhea
VIRUS							
Adenovirus	x		x		x		respiratory disease
Bovine leukosis virus (BLV)		x		x		blood	lymphoma
Bovine respiratory syncytial virus (BRSV)			x		x		respiratory disease
Bovine viral diarrhea (BVD)	x	x	x	x			respiratory disease
Coronavirus	x		x		x		diarrhea
Infectious bovine rhinotracheitis (IBR)			x	x	x		respiratory disease
Parainfluenza type 3 (PI3)			x		x		respiratory disease
Reovirus					x		respiratory disease
Rotavirus	x						diarrhea

1 - Formerly called *Haemophilus somnus*.
2 - Formerly called *Pasteurella haemolytica*.
3 - Other, less common, *Mycoplasma* species that may cause respiratory and joint infections include *M. californicum*, and *M. canadense*.
4 - Airborne transmission by inhalation of dust is suspected as an additional route.

APPENDICES

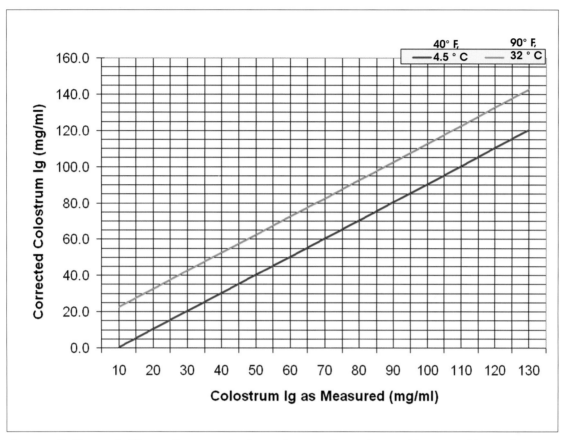

Appendix Figure 1. Correcting a colostrometer reading of mg of Ig per ml based on colostrum at 40 °F (4.5°C) or 90°F (32°C).

Appen. table 1. Molecular weights and recommended concentration of common ingredients in oral rehydration solutions.

Ingredient	MW[1] (g/mol)	Concentration[2] mmol/L	Concentration[2] g/L
Glucose (dextrose)[3]	180	< 200	< 36
Glycine[3]	75	10 to 40	0.75 to 3.0
Sodium (Na)	23	70 to 145	1.61 to 3.3
Chloride (Cl)	35	50 to 100	1.8 to 3.5
Potassium (K)	39	20 to 30	0.8 to 1.2
Sodium bicarbonate[4]	84	50 to 80	4.2 to 6.7
Sodium citrate[4]	294	50 to 80	14.7 to 23.5
Sodium acetate[4]	136	50 to 80	6.8 to 10.9

Source: Adapted from Electrolytes for Scouring Calves, Penn State Cooperative Extension Factsheet DAS 05-102.
1 - Molecular weight in grams per mole.
2 - Useful conversion: 1 quart is equal to 0.95 liter.
3 - Total of glucose and glycine not to exceed 200 mmol/L.
4 - Recommendation of 50 to 80 mmol/L is the total alkalinizing ability from all sources.

It can be difficult to compare oral rehydration solutions due to the different units that are used. Most solutions are expressed on a percentage basis; however mmol/L, mg/ml or mEq/L are also used. To convert concentrations from g/L or percentage to mmol/L, the molecular weight of each ingredient must be known. The table above contains the molecular weights for common ingredients to help you compare electrolyte products. To make the conversion from g/L to mmol/L, divide the concentration in g/L by the respective molecular weight and multiply by 1000 (which will convert from mol to mmol). For example, if a product contains 3 g/L of sodium, divide 3 by 23 and then multiply by 1000. This product provides 130 mmol/L of sodium. Converting grams or percentages to mmol/L is the most accurate way to compare various products. Molar equivalencies (mEq) are calculated based on the charge of an ion. Sodium, chloride, and potassium have a net charge of 1, so the mEq/L value is the same as mmol/L.

Aside from individual ingredient composition, another measure used for comparing products is the strong ion difference (SID), which is calculated as the concentration of sodium and potassium minus the concentration of chloride. The recommended range for SID is 50 to 80 mEq/L.

Appen Table 2. Comparing oral rehydration products.[1]

Product	Company	Glucose	Glycine	Na	Cl	K	Sodium Bicarbonate	Sodium Citrate	Sodium Acetate
						mmo/L			
Advance Arrest	MS Specialty Nutrition	97	0	40	*	7	*	0	0
Advance Pro-Lyte Plus	MS Specialty Nutrition	200	*	104	*	23	*	0	0
Blue Ribbon	Merrick's Inc.	200	*	144	*	20	0	*	0
Bluelite C	TechMix, Inc.	*	*	104	*	38	0	*	0
Bounce Back	Manna Pro	166	0	136	112	9	36	0	0
Calf Quencher	Vedco	397	0	134	76	23	81	0	0
Calf Restart One-4	TechMix, Inc.	*	*	261	*	153	0	0	0
Calf-Gel 95	Van Beek Scientific, LLC	*	0	39	*	9	*	*	0
Calf-Lyte	Bimeda	397	0	127	71	22	77	0	0
C.H.E.E.R.S.[2]	Nouriche Nutrition Ltd.	40	40	90	50	30	0	*	*
Comeback	AgriPharm	*	*	112	*	24	0	0	0
Deliver with Dialine	AgriLabs	82	0	77	16	14	37	0	0
Diaque	Boehringer Ingelheim	156	7	87	54	12	Total alkalinizing ability of 45		
Electrolyte with Thickener	DVM Formula (Vets Plus)	132	25	110	50	20	80	0	0
Electrolyte HE with Vitamins	DVM Formula (Vets Plus)	242	25	110	50	20	80	0	0
ElectrolytesPlus	Sav-A-Caf (Milk Products)	250	30	117	*	7	*	0	0
Ener-Lyte	Aspen	*	*	127	*	19	*	0	0
Entrolyte	Pfizer	166	22	95	46	23	80	0	0
Entrolyte HE	Pfizer	450	38	90	45	23	78	0	0
Formula 911	Advantech	*	*	127	*	19	*	0	0
Hydrafeed[3]	A&L Laboratories	*	32	115	62	11	86	14	0
Hydra-Lyte	Vet-A-Mix	405	16	78	45	30	0	3	60
Hy-sorb	Bimeda	56	40	99	65	10	40	9	0
Nutri-Sorb	AgriPharm	62	0	70	63	16	23	0	0
One Day Response	Farnam	0	*	65	*	10	*	*	0
Re-sorb[4]	Pfizer	129	45	80	80	17	0	2	0
Revitilyte	Vets Plus, Inc.	174	25	110	50	20	80	0	0
Revitilyte-Gelling	Vets Plus, Inc.	132	25	110	50	20	80	0	0

Source: Calculated from information listed in the Compendium of Veterinary Products, 2005 and from product labels.
1 - This listing may not include every available product. Where trade names appear, no discrimination is intended, and no endorsement by Penn State Cooperative Extension is implied.
* Insufficient information to calculate.
2 - Contains maltodextrin (glucose polymer).
3 - Contains 63 g of lactose (glucose and galactose).
4 - Citrate sources are potassium citrate and citric acid, not sodium citrate.